IRELAND'S WETLANDS AND THEIR BIRDS

IRELAND'S WETLANDS AND THEIR BIRDS

By Clive Hutchinson

IRISH WILDBIRD CONSERVANCY
1979

First published 1979 by
Irish Wildbird Conservancy,
c/o Royal Irish Academy,
19 Dawson Street,
Dublin 2.

ISBN 0 9504454 4 4

Printed by the *Leinster Leader Limited*, Naas, Co. Kildare.

What would the world be, once bereft
Of wet and of wildness? Let them be left,
O let them be left, wildness and wet;
Long live the weeds and the wilderness yet.

Gerard Manley Hopkins

CONTENTS

FOREWORD

It gives me much pleasure to respond to the invitation by the Irish Wildbird Conservancy to introduce this splendidly produced book to the fast growing numbers of our people who appreciate the value of our natural heritage of wetlands and waterfowl. I must pay a special tribute to the author for the detailed knowledge of and dedication to his subject which are so manifest in this well-illustrated and comprehensive survey of Irish wetlands and wetland birds.

I should not omit to include in my appreciation all those who have contributed to the making of this definitive work on the wetlands of Ireland as a whole: it is indeed a noteworthy instance of co-operation in the interest of the waterfowl of our island habitat.

I am particularly gratified that my Department has been able to make a contribution to the material contained in this book. To all who share in my appreciation of and concern for conservation of this very important feature of our wildlife heritage, I strongly commend this work.

Minister for Fisheries and Forestry

ACKNOWLEDGMENTS

The accounts of wetlands and of waterfowl distribution in this book could not have been written without the hard work of approximately a hundred people, most of them spare-time birdwatchers, who participated in the *Wetlands Enquiry* organised by the Irish Wildbird Conservancy to survey the birds of Irish wetlands. Unfortunately these are too many to be acknowledged individually but they will be pleased, I hope, to see how their enthusiasm for counting birds in all kinds of weather has contributed to our knowledge of bird distribution throughout the country.

Most of the counters have been amateurs, but this book has benefited greatly from the co-operation and assistance of the Department of Fisheries and Forestry. Data collected from aerial surveys and ground counts by officers of the Forest and Wildlife Service were made available to the Irish Wildbird Conservancy and grants were paid towards travelling expenses incurred by members of the I.W.C. in counting certain areas. The support of the Forest and Wildlife Service for the survey work on which this book is based has been invaluable and is gratefully acknowledged, but I wish to thank the Minister for Fisheries and Forestry particularly for his assistance in subventing the publishing cost of this book and thereby helping to make it available to a wider public.

I also wish to thank the Commission of the European Economic Communities for subsidising printing costs and the Royal Irish Academy for providing grants from the Praeger Fund to promote fieldwork.

The collection of over 2,000 counts posed enormous data handling problems for a spare-time organiser as I was. The difficulties would probably have been insurmountable but for the assistance of Dr. Raymond O'Connor in arranging computer processing and writing the programs required to prepare many of the tables, maps and diagrams which follow. John Rochford and Jim Fitzharris helped in the tedious task of coding the original count cards for keypunching.

The I.W.C. survey only involved the Republic. Material from Northern Ireland was provided by Chris Bailey, Niall Carson, T. Ennis (on behalf of the Northern Ireland Ornithologists' Club), A. Ferguson, J. S. Furphy, W. Hilditch and Arthur Irvine (on behalf of the National Trust for Northern Ireland).

Dr. David Cabot made available data collected by the Irish Wildfowl Conservancy and now in the files of An Foras Forbartha. George Atkinson-Willes supplied copies of wildfowl counts carried out in the 1950s and early 1960s for the Wildfowl Trust in Slimbridge.

The entire text was read and commented on by Dr. Raymond O'Connor, Oscar Merne and Ken Preston. Parts of the text were also read by Frank King, A. J. Prater, Major R. F. Ruttledge and L. Stapleton. The text for the section on the north-east of Ireland was largely rewritten by J. S. Furphy. I am grateful to them all for their expert advice. Needless to add, any errors are totally my own responsibility. As well as sharing my enthusiasm for waterfowl and their haunts, my wife also provided support by reading the proofs, a task for which I am completely unsuited. I am grateful to her and to T. C. Kelly who also read the proofs.

The pages of the book have been enlivened by the pencil drawings of Gordon D'Arcy, the wash illustrations of Vincent Sheridan, the vignettes of Killian Mullarney and the photographs of Oscar Merne (pages 62 and 76) and Richard Mills (all other photographs). I am sure their art will attract more readers to learn about Irish wetlands than would otherwise have read this book. The Managing Editor of the magazine *British Birds* gave permission for the reproduction of several vignettes which first appeared in that publication.

Clive Hutchinson
November 1978

INTRODUCTION

What are wetlands and why should anyone write a book about them? The questions are fundamental as the word 'wetland' is modern jargon, hazy and ill-defined, and the value of the habitat encompassed by the term is not universally accepted in Ireland. The word covers damp and marshy land, rivers, lakes, estuaries, inter-tidal beaches and the shallow marine waters in bays around the coast. A wetland, in effect, is any damp or inundated land apart from the open sea. Even this definition is not very satisfactory, for where does the open sea begin? Is Dublin Bay a wetland? Or is Bantry Bay? In the long run the question becomes academic, but in general in this book wetlands are taken as extending as far out to sea as ducks, other than sea-ducks like Eiders and Common Scoters, occur.

The most important reasons for writing a book about Irish wetlands are because they are extremely rich habitats in terms of the number and density of animal species they support and because they are so vulnerable to destruction by drainage, infill, refuse dumping and pollution. Unfortunately, an appreciation of the value of wetlands is still too rare in Ireland. For too many people, and too many institutions, marshes and estuaries are wastelands. How many rusting motor-cars, how many tons of garbage, how many gallons of effluent are happily disposed of in the mud? And yet, alongside the attitudes that permit this despoilation to continue there exists the general interest in wildfowl and waders of shooting men and a growing number of the public. This benevolent interest, and the commitment to the conservation of wetlands of a lesser number of people, has been reflected in tighter conditions for the granting of planning permission by local authorities to potentially polluting industries. But industrial development and refuse dumping continue to take away prime estuarine mudflat and arterial drainage still obliterates some of the best remaining wetlands in the west. At this stage in Irish development a register of wetlands is urgently needed setting out the importance of each area so that planners can take note of their conservation value and in future years changes in the significance of individual wetlands can be monitored. The first part of this book consists of such a register, expressed in terms of the number of wildfowl and waders occurring at each site. Ideally a register of wetlands should classify sites in terms of all the organisms known to occur at each area, but in Ireland, as elsewhere, far more is known of the numbers and distribution of birds than of any other group. The second part of this book is a species by species account of the numbers, distribution and migrations of the birds which occur at Irish wetlands.

The data on which the wetland and species accounts are based are drawn mainly from wildfowl and wader counts carried out in the Republic of Ireland by members of the Irish Wildbird Conservancy and by the Forest and Wildlife Service as part of the *Wetlands Enquiry,* a detailed survey of wetlands and their birds, and in Northern Ireland by the Northern Ireland Ornithologists' Club and other organisations and individuals for the *Birds of Estuaries Enquiry,* sponsored by three British research and conservation organisations, the British Trust for Ornithology, the Wildfowl Trust and the Royal Society for the Protection of Birds. The book also draws, however, on all the other wildfowl and wader counts of which the IWC has records and on many other published and unpublished records.

Wildfowl counting began in Ireland in the late 1940s and early 1950s when monthly counts were carried out at a number of locations, mostly close to the centres of population at Dublin and Belfast, under the auspices of the Wildfowl Trust at Slimbridge in England. Much valuable data was collected but very little use was made of it and none was published. There was a hiatus in the late 1950s and early 1960s, but a sudden revival in 1964 and 1965. In 1964-65 the first of a quite remarkable series of counts of the huge duck populations of the Lough Neagh basin was completed by the Northern Ireland Ornithologists' Club and in December 1965 the Irish Wildfowl Committee was founded. This organisation, which became the Irish Wildfowl Conservancy in 1967 and was absorbed into the Irish Wildbird Conservancy in January 1969, sponsored monthly wildfowl counts, large-scale duck counts to coincide with international censuses and special goose surveys. The increasing interest in wildfowl studies in Ireland mirrored a similar development throughout Europe. The International Waterfowl Research Bureau, a body with the aims of promoting and undertaking research into wildfowl, had been founded in 1947 as a purely European organisation. Now its membership includes countries from all over the globe. As part of its development the IWRB began a series of January international wildfowl counts in 1967. From 1969 to 1973 counts were carried out in November as well and since 1975 they have been carried out in March. Ireland has participated in all these international surveys, with the exception of that in January 1968 when restrictions on access to land because of the fear of an epidemic of foot-and-mouth disease prevented adequate coverage. In addition quite large-scale surveys were carried out in the Republic in March 1968 to replace the abandoned January count, and in February 1970, 1971 and 1972. These last were carried out early in the month, just after the end of the shooting season, for comparison with the January counts which many people argued were inaccurate because of the level of disturbance.

All these counts were of value, but their chief importance was in identifying the more important wetlands. They were no substitute for the monthly counts which Northern Ireland ornithologists had been making at Lough Neagh, Lough Foyle and Strangford Lough and which a few observers in the Republic had been carrying out at several wetlands as well. Monthly counts, provided they are carried out by the same observer, have two great advantages. Firstly, the very frequency of visits to a wetland makes an observer aware of what birds he may expect and where they may be when disturbed. Secondly, counts at monthly intervals give a much better picture of the importance of a site for migrating as well as for wintering birds. And of course when monthly counts are made at a large number of wetlands one can draw some conclusions as to the timing of migration and the extent to which birds move, even within the country. So, in 1971-72 the *Wetlands Enquiry* commenced, initially as a survey of estuaries only, in conjunction with the British *Birds of Estuaries Enquiry,* but from 1972-73 as a survey of both inland and coastal wetlands based on monthly counts.

The basic recording form was the Wetland Bird Counting Card (Fig. 1). On this card there are spaces for filling in the count of each common species seen, or placing a tick if a species is seen but not counted. In practice, during the survey gulls were not usually counted, but in practically all cases waders and other water birds were

WETLAND NORTH BULL		GRID REFERENCE 0 2 3 3 7		DAY 1 8	MONTH 1 1	YEAR 1 9 7 3
OBSERVER C.D. Hutchinson J.M. Rochford		COUNTY DUBLIN		AREA COVERED Sutton to Fairview		
COUNT TIMES 11.00 Start G.M.T. 16.45 Finish G.M.T.		ACTUAL HIGH TIDE 17.30 G.M.T.		TIDE/WATER LEVEL Out to full in		

Species		Species		Species		Species	
Gt. Cr. Grebe	5	Eider		Snipe	7	Ruff	
Little Grebe		Red-br. Merg.	25	Jack Snipe		G.B.h. Gull	✓
Cormorant	8	Shelduck	107	Curlew	3,075	L.B.h. Gull	
Shag		Grey Lag. G.		Whimbrel		Herring Gull	✓
Grey Heron	14	White-fr. G.		Bl. t. Godwit		Comm. Gull	✓
Mallard	70	Brent G.	138	Bar. t. Godwit	1,065	Blk. hd. Gull	✓
Teal	1,368	Barnacle G.		Green Sand			
Gadwall		Mute Swan		Wood Sand			
Wigeon	2,457	Whooper S.		Common Sand			
Pintail	229	Bewick's S.		Redshank	1,410		
Shoveler	216	Coot		Spotted Red.			
Scaup		Oystercatcher	2,590	Greenshank	5		
Tufted Duck		Lapwing	7	Knot	8,150		
Pochard		Ringed Plover		Little Stint			
Goldeneye	10	Grey Plover	231	Dunlin	7,120		
Long-t. Duck		Golden Plover		Curlew Sand			
Com. Scoter	6	Turnstone	65	Sanderling			

Fig. 1. Wetland count card.

censused as well as wildfowl. Counts were carried out by carefully selected observers and the accuracy of counting techniques was assessed by encouraging counters to make comparative estimates of individual flocks of birds. The results of these tests showed quite a low level of variation between the most practised counters. The significance of even a low variation in estimates was further reduced by the policy of ensuring, so far as possible, that counts at individual wetlands were carried out by the same observer. In 1972-73, the second year of the survey, monthly aerial counts of the Shannon and a number of other western areas were commenced by the Forest and Wildlife Service. The data from these counts were invaluable in assessing the importance of many sites which are either relatively remote or difficult to approach from the ground. Since waders were counted as well as wildfowl from 1973-74 onwards special techniques had to be developed to cope with the enormous amount of data being collected very rapidly. Counts were made from a three or four seater aircraft with wings above the fuselage to facilitate visibility. Two observers usually carried out the counts, recording data on a cassette recorder for subsequent transcription. In addition, comparative counts were carried out at the Little Brosna, Co. Offaly and the Fergus estuary, Co. Clare by observers in the air and on the ground to assess the accuracy of each method of counting. Interestingly, the results in all cases showed that aerial counts produced greater totals of birds but that ground counts produced larger counts of some of the scarcer species. Clearly the aerial counter saw more birds but had difficulty in separating the species in large mixed flocks. In the analysis of the count data these difficulties were largely ignored, for only at a very few wetlands were counts regularly carried out from both ground and air. When this happened the higher count for each species was generally taken as the more acceptable figure for analysis.

The survey was remarkably successful. During the four years a total of 2,001 counts was received for 289 wetlands in the Republic. The analysis of this data would have been impossible but for the computer processing arranged by Dr. Raymond O'Connor. The essential data on each count card was transcribed onto a data coding form and then punched for processing. The initial output was next checked against the original cards and any errors corrected. Only then was the data acceptable for summary, analysis and the compilation of many of the tables included in this book.

Table 1
Number of count cards returned for each year of the *Wetlands Enquiry*

1971-72	323
1972-73	569
1973-74	570
1974-75	549
	2,001

So what are the results of all this work? On an international scale it has helped us to assist in the surveys which are attempting to provide baseline criteria for establishing the international importance of individual wetlands. It is now considered that any wetland holding at least 10,000 ducks, 20,000 waders or one per cent of the flyway population of individual species is of international importance. Ireland is part of the north-west European wildfowl flyway and the west European wader flyway. On a national scale we can now estimate the Irish wintering population of most wildfowl and wader species. At present it seems appropriate to consider a wetland holding five per cent or more of the Irish total as of national importance. The criteria for such areas are listed in Table 2. The most important outcome of this work is the production of this book which presents summarised accounts of the most important wetlands and the distribution and numbers of their birds in far greater detail than has ever been published before.

Table 2
Criteria for identifying concentrations of international and national importance

	Inter-national	National		Inter-national	National
Mallard	10,000	1,750	Brent Goose	120	120
Teal	1,500	1,500	Barnacle Goose	550	200
Wigeon	4,000	4,000	Oystercatcher	5,600	1,500
Pintail	500	250	Ringed Plover	200	100
Shoveler	200	200	Grey Plover	300	100
Scaup	1,500	100	Curlew	1,500	?
Tufted Duck	2,500	1,500	Black-tailed Godwit	400	400
Pochard	5,000	1,750	Bar-tailed Godwit	900	750
Shelduck	1,250	400	Redshank	1,250	750
Mute Swan	1,200	150	Spotted Redshank	100	—
Whooper Swan	175	175	Greenshank	100	—
Bewick's Swan	100	100	Knot	6,000	2,500
Greylag Goose	750	50	Dunlin	12,000	5,000
White-fronted Goose	120	120	Sanderling	100	100

Note: No population estimates are available for some species, such as Lapwing and Golden Plover, so these have been excluded from this table.

THE WETLANDS

EAST AND MIDLANDS

For the purpose of this book the east and midlands is defined as the area of Ireland east of the River Shannon, south of a line from Lough Allen to Newry and north of a line from Limerick to the Wicklow/Wexford border (Fig. 2). It includes south Leitrim and Cavan, Monaghan, Louth, Meath, Westmeath, Longford, Dublin, Wicklow, Kildare, Laois, Offaly and the northern halves of Tipperary, Kilkenny and Carlow. The coast from Carlingford Lough in the north to Dublin is a low-lying stretch of sand-dunes or low cliffs with wide sandy beaches, indented with a series of estuaries which hold very large numbers of wintering ducks and waders. South of Dublin the coast is equally low-lying but no muddy estuaries break the broad sweep of the bays between the promontories at Dalkey, Bray Head, Wicklow Head, Mizen Point and Arklow Head, though brackish lagoons are enclosed by dunes at Kilcoole and Broad Lough.

Inland, the great granite mass of the Leinster Chain dominates the landscape south of Dublin. The coastal strip between Dublin and Wicklow Head is no more than ten kilometres wide. Behind this lowland area the mountains run from the southern suburbs of Dublin to New Ross in Wexford. The few small lakes in the mountains are unimportant for waterfowl, mostly being deep and acidic. North and west of Dublin, and west of the Leinster Chain, the landscape is low as far as the Shannon; only the drumlin swarms in south Leitrim, Cavan and Monaghan relieve the flatness significantly. Yet there is remarkable diversity in the landscape.

North of Dublin the finest pasture land in Ireland is found in the limestone country of Meath. This fertile cattle-fattening belt extends west into Westmeath and south into Dublin and Kildare. The land is well drained and contains very few wetlands; only the artificial reservoir at Poulaphouca on the eastern fringe of the lowlands supports even small numbers of wildfowl. But the rich farmlands change gradually into a poorly drained area of raised bog interspersed with cultivated land, the first indication being noticeable only thirty kilometres from Dublin. As one nears the Shannon the proportion of bog increases. In the region where the lakes of Westmeath, Longford and Cavan still harbour great flocks of ducks there was a vast extent of fen vegetation on the fringes of numerous lakes some 5,000 years ago. The lakes shrank as the fens invaded, gradually followed by other plants, and the accumulation of vegetable matter as the lakes dried up ultimately produced the raised bogs which now surround the most important wetlands in the area. Lakes such as Derravaragh, Iron and Owel are shallow and rich in feeding.

Farther north and west the lakes of Leitrim, Cavan and Monaghan are quite different. Here the landscape is dominated by drumlins and the hollows between them are mostly badly drained and filled with small lakes or bogs. The most remarkable examples of these lakes are in the Lough Oughter system, a series of lakes formed where the River Erne has spread out into a complex series of channels separating drumlins from each other. These lakes all support small numbers of diving ducks and many have herds of Whooper Swans as well.

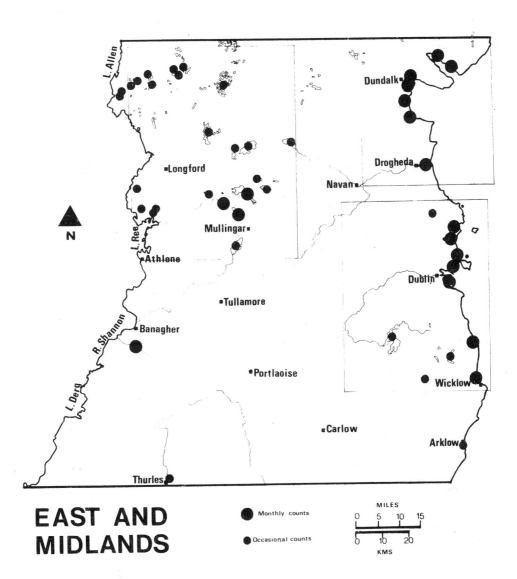

**EAST AND
MIDLANDS**

● Monthly counts

● Occasional counts

MILES
0   5   10   15

0   10   20
KMS

Fig. 2. Extent of coverage at wetlands in the East and Midlands

However, the most important sections of this region for wetland birds are the coastal estuaries and the midland lakes south of the drumlin belt. On the coast the greatest threats to the birds are the spread of *Spartina,* a plant notorious for choking estuarine mudflat, and proposals for land reclamation, either for industrial development or as an easy solution to the problem of refuse disposal. *Spartina* is present on all the estuaries and has encroached most seriously at Lurgangreen, towards the southern end of Dundalk Bay, and at Baldoyle Bay. It is a tough grass which expands on mudflats at the rate of one metre radially per annum. It has the effect of eliminating the invertebrates in the mud below, thereby removing food for wading birds. Moreover, birds do not roost in a *Spartina* marsh. The other major threat to the east coast estuaries is a consequence of the growth of Dublin city. The Dublin Port and Docks Board published proposals in 1972 for filling in much of Dublin Bay to provide a huge industrial estate at the hub of the city. These proposals envisaged the reclamation of much of the mudflats on the north side of the bay and the creation of a landlocked lagoon between the North Bull island and the mainland. Dublin County Council has plans for the dumping of domestic refuse at the estuaries of Rogerstown, Malahide and Baldoyle. At the time of writing Rogerstown has been devastated by the creation of an extensive dump and this must inevitably reduce the number of birds using the area.

The large midland lakes are all threatened by euthrophication. Towns have grown around several of the larger lakes and domestic sewage discharged untreated into the lakes has been blamed for causing the problem. Effluent from farms, particularly pig farms, has also contributed to enrichment. To date the effects of euthrophication have been more marked on the trout fishing of the region than on the birds.

The birds occurring in Dublin and Wicklow are well known and their status has recently been summarised (Hutchinson 1975). Much less has been published on those which occur in Louth but this is changing with the publication since 1974 of an annual bird report for the county. Nothing of significance has been published on the birds of the inland counties of this area.

The most numerous wetland species in the area are the Oystercatcher and Dunlin. Oystercatchers are most numerous in autumn, when over 30,000 stop to feed while on passage; only about 13,000 remain to winter. Dunlin are the most abundant winter birds with a regular population in excess of 25,000. The numbers of Lapwing, Golden Plover and Curlew wintering in the region are unknown as so many occur away from wetlands, but certainly exceed 10,000 in each case. The only other species with a population of 10,000 or more in the region are the Bar-tailed Godwit (10,000) and Knot (12,000). The totals for each are respectively 70% and 30% of the Irish winter populations of these species. The most abundant wildfowl are Wigeon (up to 7,500) and Pochard (6,000 in autumn). Wigeon arrive in their largest numbers in November and January, but Pochard build up on Lough Derravaragh early in autumn, perhaps to moult. The average numbers of certain species recorded over the four years from 1971-72 to 1974-5 at the main wetlands are shown at Tables 3 and 4. The figures given are the average for the month in which the largest numbers were recorded in each case.

Large numbers of gulls use the estuaries as well as ducks, geese and waders, but very few counts have been made of them. Flocks of over 5,000 Herring Gulls feed at each of the two main refuse dumps in Dublin Bay and up to 2,000 Common Gulls and

VINCENT SHERIDAN

8,000 Black-headed Gulls winter in the bay. The numbers occurring at the other wetlands have only been counted very occasionally. Great Northern and Red-throated Divers occur in small numbers in the outer reaches of the estuaries. Great Crested Grebes winter in Malahide Estuary and Dublin Bay. Common Scoter winter in Dublin Bay, along much of the coast between Dublin and Clogher Head and off Arklow on the Wicklow coast. Velvet Scoter occur in small numbers in late autumn. The estuaries have very few breeding waterfowl: Mallard, Shelduck and Ringed Plover are the main species. Inland, Mallard and Tufted Duck are the most prominent.

The major wetlands are treated in some detail in the remainder of this chapter, dealing first with the coastal wetlands, running from north to south, and then with those inland.

Carlingford Lough

Carlingford Lough is not an estuary at all but a fjord-like sea lough which was scoured by a glacier during the Pleistocene. The mouth is shallower than much of the lough itself, a characteristic of all true fjords, and the bay is surrounded by moraines. The principal areas of muddy shoreline are near the mouth of the lough and in the narrow neck running up to Newry town (Fig. 3).

The figures at Table 3 and 4 show that this area has the fourth largest concentrations of wildfowl and waders on the east coast, but it holds no population of international importance (as defined in the Introduction). It has wintering flocks of Teal, Wigeon, Shelduck, Brent Geese, Oystercatchers, Curlew, Redshanks and Dunlin

(Table 5). It also holds up to 220 Mallard, quite a sizeable concentration for any Irish estuary or sea lough. The most interesting feature of Carlingford Lough's avifauna is its flock of Scaup which is of national importance, representing at least 25% of the Irish winter population. Unfortunately, the numbers have declined from 2,500 in the mid-1960s to between 500 and 1,000 in the years from 1971-72 to 1974-75. There are no conservation measures in force on either side of the lough.

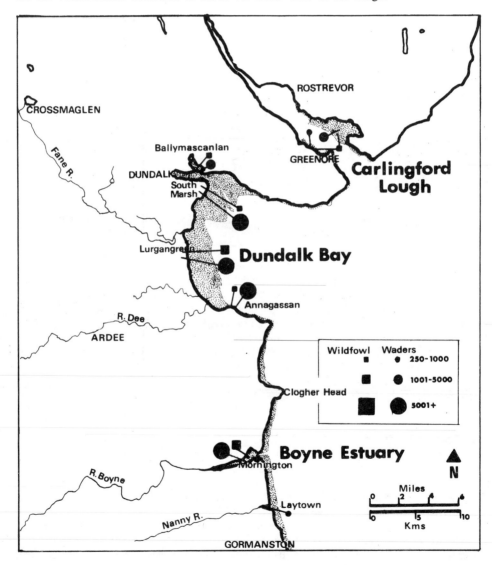

Fig. 3. Principal concentrations of wildfowl and waders in Louth and Meath

Dundalk Bay

Although fed by the Castletown and Fane rivers, Dundalk Bay is not primarily an estuary, but a broad bay with a very extensive and rather coarse, muddy inter-tidal area extending for nearly twenty kilometres from Ballymascanlan to Annagassan (Fig. 3). At low tide the 4,500 hectares of mudflat and sand provides feeding for the largest concentrations of Oystercatchers and Bar-tailed Godwits in Ireland. The winter population of Oystercatchers is about 10,000 birds, representing 2% of the west European population; in autumn the peak is nearly 27,000. In international terms the Bar-tailed Godwit flock is much more significant, representing 7% of the west European population. Other species occurring in numbers of international importance are Curlew, Redshank, Knot and Dunlin, and the autumn flock of Golden Plover, which in some years can reach 13,000 is one of the largest in Ireland.

As will be clear from Tables 3 and 4 the importance of Dundalk Bay is mainly as a wader site. The numbers of waders occurring here are far higher than at any other site on the east coast. In Ireland as a whole only the Shannon Estuary and Strangford Lough have had more waders recorded. On the Atlantic coast of Europe and north Africa it ranks among the top fifteen estuaries. The numbers of wildfowl, mainly ducks, are comparatively low, though the bay ranks third in importance on the east coast (Table 3). However, there is considerable diversity of wildfowl: 13 species were recorded in winter 1974-75.

At low tide waders spread out over the available mudflat which, despite the expansion of *Spartina* at Lurgangreen, is still enormous and relatively secure. At high tide there are several roosts, much the most important of which are on salt marsh at the South Marsh and at Lurgangreen (Fig. 3) where the majority of the waders rest at high tide. Smaller roosts are located on sand banks near Ballymascanlan and on shingle shore at Annagassan. Teal and Wigeon tend to congregate at the South Marsh and Lurgangreen; Mallard, which occur in numbers up to 700 in autumn, 300 in winter, congregate west of Ballymascanlan and off Annagassan.

Ballymascanlan Bay and part of the salt marsh at Lurgangreen are protected by the prohibition of shooting under Section 24 (2) of the Wildlife Act, 1976.

Boyne Estuary

The Boyne Estuary below Drogheda town extends for about five kilometres before reaching the sea, but the river is narrow with restricted inter-tidal mudflat, much of which is being reclaimed, as far as Mornington. Below Mornington the inter-tidal flats are more extensive where the river takes a meander behind the sand dunes at Baltray.

The estuary ranks seventh for wildfowl and fourth for waders among the east coast wetlands (Tables 3 and 4). It holds flocks of much the same species which winter on the other estuaries, but in smaller numbers, though the flock of wintering Black-tailed Godwits (up to 250) is the largest on the east coast north of Wexford. Though the wetland is of considerable local importance it contains no populations of national significance.

The western half of the estuary is protected by a no-shooting Order.

Laytown

South of the Boyne, the estuary of the Nanny river at Laytown holds fluctuating numbers of waders and a few ducks. The wader species which occur are those common at the Boyne and it seems likely that the parties of up to 40 Redshanks, 200 Knot and 600 Dunlin which occur at Laytown on occasion have come from the Boyne.

Rogerstown

Rogerstown Estuary is a broad, muddy estuary at the mouth of a small river which meanders across farmland before broadening out into an inter-tidal area of some 360 hectares. At its mouth it is protected from storms by a terminal sand spit. The estuary is divided in two by a railway causeway. Above the causeway the mud is soft and edged with salt marsh on the south-west side. Below the causeway the mudflat is coarser and scarred with mussel beds.

The estuary is the second most important on the east coast for wildfowl and the third most important for waders (Tables 3 and 4). It is of international importance as a wintering site for Brent Geese and of national importance for Pintail and Shelduck (Table 5). It also has large wintering flocks of Wigeon, Teal, Mute Swans, Oystercatchers, Curlew, Redshanks, Knot and Dunlin (Table 5).

This is one of the few estuaries for which we have comparative counts from the 1950s. Wigeon numbers fell from peak numbers of 700-1,850 in the early 1950s to 800-1,000 in the late 1960s, but increased each winter after the prohibition of shooting from 1971 to a peak of 2,300 in 1973-74. Teal, which were very scarce in the 1950s, increased enormously to peak at 800 in 1971-72, 500 in 1972-73 and 1,500 in 1973-74. Pintail and Shoveler, formerly almost unknown at Rogerstown, also increased during the 1970s. The estuary now holds as many wintering ducks as it has held within living memory.

The future of the estuary must be in grave doubt. A recent study (Fahy et al 1975) concluded that the estuary has become subject to increasing organic pollution, that algal growth has increased and that further increases in nutrients would cause undesirable extension of algal mats in the estuary. The authors recorded pollution from the pumping of pig slurry directly onto the mudflats, from fertilizer running off the surrounding farmland and from the Dublin County Council tip.

Table 3

Maximum numbers of ducks, geese and swans recorded at east coast wetlands, 1971-72 to 1974-75 (NC indicates no count, + indicates incomplete count)

	1971-72	1972-73	1973-74	1974-75
North Bull	7,400	8,000	7,700	6,700
Rogerstown	3,300	3,300	5,300	3,100
Dundalk Bay	NC	NC	2,152	4,062
Carlingford Lough	800+	1,200+	2,500	2,500
Malahide Estuary	1,900	1,500	1,100	1,500
Broad Lough	400	1,600	1,500	1,600
Boyne Estuary	700	900	900	1,300
Kilcoole	600	500	100	NC

Table 4

Maximum numbers of waders recorded at east coast wetlands, 1971-72 to 1974-75 (NC indicates no count, + indicates incomplete count).

	1971-72	1972-73	1973-74	1974-75
Dundalk Bay	NC	NC	48,800	50,100
North Bull	29,700	27,500	36,600	27,600
Rogerstown	6,000	5,000	7,800	3,600
Carlingford Lough	2,900+	3,100+	7,700	7,000
Boyne Estuary	5,000	5,000	7,400	6,300
Malahide Estuary	2,600	6,200	4,800	4,200
Broad Lough	1,600	2,700	1,100	1,000
Kilcoole	1,500	1,100	1,500	1,000

Malahide Estuary

Malahide Estuary has some similar features to Rogerstown (Fig. 4). A narrow river, the Broad Meadow, wends through Dublin farmland before widening out into the estuary. Sand dunes almost close the exit to the sea. A railway causeway bisects the estuary. But the estuary behind the railway causeway is very different. The water level drops only a few centimetres on the ebb tide and the only mud exposed is around some small grassy islands at the head of the estuary near Lissenhall Bridge. On the seaward side of the causeway the inter-tidal mudflats are quite extensive and resemble the mussel scarred flats west of the railway line at Rogerstown.

This combination of typical, muddy estuary and sheltered lagoon provides a diversity of habitat which supports a waterfowl community rather different from that of the neighbouring Dublin estuaries. Great Crested Grebes (up to 60 in November), Goldeneye (up to 150) and Red-breasted Mergansers (up to 100) occur in larger numbers and some rarer species of grebe and diving duck are recorded occasionally. At the head of the estuary Ruffs and scarcer waders such as Little Stints and Curlew Sandpipers feed each autumn on the soft mud around the islands. On the mudflats below the causeway Brent Geese occur in winter in numbers which entitle the estuary to be classified as of international importance. Wigeon and Shelduck also winter there and medium sized flocks of the commoner wader species are usually present.

On the basis of the number of birds recorded there Malahide Estuary ranks fifth amongst the east coast estuaries for wildfowl and sixth for waders (Tables 3 and 4).

Above the causeway the open water is used for sailing and water-skiing. There is some disturbance of the diving ducks but it appears to be at a tolerable level in winter when most of the birds are present. Close to the islands below Lissenhall Bridge the construction of a dwelling house is likely to add to the pressure for reclamation, a process which would be disastrous for the birds of this section of the estuary. The estuary below the causeway is threatened by proposals to dump domestic refuse near Corballis.

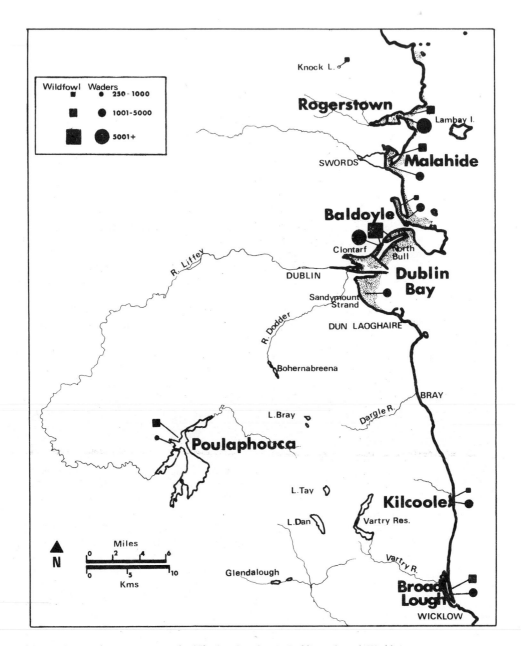

Fig. 4. Principal concentrations of wildfowl and waders in Dublin and north Wicklow

Table 5

Average numbers of the most common species recorded in the peak month at each major east coast wetland, 1971-72 to 1974-75. The peak month is the month with the highest average numbers. Two asterisks indicate a concentration of international importance, one asterisk a concentration of national importance.

	Carling-ford L.	Dundalk Bay	Boyne Estuary	Rogers-town	Malahide Estuary	North Bull	Kilcoole	Broad Lough
Teal	300	700	100	500	100	1,200	—	300
Wigeon	500	1,800	600	1,100	400	2,600	400	500
Pintail	—	100	—	200*	—	300*	—	—
Shoveler	—	—	—	100	—	300**	—	—
Shelduck	100	300	100	600*	200	400*	—	—
Brent Goose	100	100	—	400**	200**	1,000**	—	—
Oystercatcher	500	26,700**	500	500	600	3,800*	—	—
Golden Plover	—	5,400	800	600	1,300	200	500	400
Curlew	900	4,200**	600	500	100	1,900**	300	400
Bar-tailed Godwit	—	7,100**	—	—	—	2,300**	—	—
Redshank	700	3,700**	500	500	400	2,400**	100	100
Knot	—	3,600*	700	1,300	800	6,700**	—	—
Dunlin	1,700	12,400**	1,400	1,300	600	7,900*	100	100

Baldoyle Bay

Baldoyle Bay, between Malahide Estuary and the North Bull, is a long narrow embayment protected from the sea by sand dunes which provide, as at the Boyne and Malahide, a superb surface for golf links. The estuary itself is choked with *Spartina* and the number of birds using the site is very small.

Up to 200 Wigeon and a few Pintail feed here in February; earlier in the winter the number is even lower. Some Brent Geese fly across from the North Bull when food is getting scarce late in the season. The wader species found are those which winter on the North Bull, but numbers are low, rarely more than 1,500 being counted.

This estuary is scheduled for refuse dumping also. Because of the impoverishment of its avifauna there would be every advantage in transferring dumping activities immediately from Rogerstown to Baldoyle.

North Bull

The North Bull is unquestionably the best documented Irish wetland. The recently published book on the natural history of the island (Jeffrey 1977) describes the extent of current knowledge of most aspects of the structure, fauna and flora of the North Bull and makes proposals for the conservation of the area. However, as a haunt of waterfowl the North Bull should not be considered in isolation, but as the roosting area for thousands of birds which use the mudflats of Dublin Bay, both north and south of the river, as a source of food.

Dublin Bay has the second largest area of sand and mudflats on this coastline, only Dundalk Bay having more (Fig. 4). The River Liffey flows into the sea in the centre of the bay between the arms of the Bull Wall and South Wall. North of the river the

Brent Geese feeding by the road at Dollymount, North Bull.

North Bull island, a low island of sand dune and salt marsh, stretches diagonally across the bay from the Bull Wall to Sutton at the base of the Howth peninsula. The area between the island and the mainland is a muddy creek, fringed with salt marsh on the edge of the island. This creek is cut at midpoint by a causeway from the island to the shore which was completed by Dublin Corporation in 1964. The creek has silted up since the causeway was constructed and now shows all the signs of salt marsh extension. A mat of *Salicornia* extends over much of the channel. More ominously, *Spartina* now grows in small clumps on the mud.

At high tide most of the wildfowl and waders in Dublin Bay roost on the salt marsh on the island. As the tide ebbs the waders spread out across the sand and mud on both sides of the bay. The majority of the ducks remain to feed in the creek between the island and the mainland, and the Brent Geese feed on the *Zostera* which grows off Kilbarrack and Sutton to the north of the island. Later in the winter, when the *Zostera* is exhausted, the geese feed on the algal mats which are spreading on the flats both north and south of the River Liffey.

The site is an internationally important wetland for Brent Geese, Curlew, Bar-tailed Godwits, Redshank and Knot (Table 4). It is of national importance for Pintail, Shoveler, Oystercatchers, Grey Plover and Dunlin. It ranks second to Dundalk Bay on this coastline in terms of the numbers of waders recorded (Table 3) and has substantially larger numbers of wildfowl than any other coastal wetland in the area (Table 3). Unquestionably, the density of birds supported by the available mudflat is much greater than at any other Irish estuary.

The wildfowl have been counted in most years since 1951 and at monthly intervals for a number of years in the early 1950s and again from the late 1960s. During these years there is no evidence of long term decrease in the numbers of any species other than those, such as Shelduck and Knot, which have decreased generally along this coast since the late 1960s. Indeed, three species, Teal, Pintail and Shoveler, have increased quite substantially over this period. The visitor to the North Bull in winter nowadays will see at least as many birds as any visitor this century.

While the North Bull is protected as a Bird Sanctuary, the area comes under continuing threat from local authorities. Dublin Corporation commenced the dumping of domestic refuse on the salt marsh several years ago, but has halted operations pending the production of a scientific report on the area under the auspices of a joint committee of An Taisce and An Foras Forbartha. Dublin Port and Docks Board has proposed plans which involve converting part of the channel into an enclosed lagoon and reclaiming much of the mudflat outside the island. The utmost vigilance will be required to ensure the survival of this remarkable wetland, the value of which ultimately derives not just from the importance of the bird populations there but from the area's proximity to the centre of Ireland's capital city.

Brent Geese in flight over causeway, North Bull

Kilcoole

Kilcoole marsh lies south of Greystones on the flat stretch of lowland behind the shingle which stretches south to Wicklow Head (Fig. 4). It consists of a series of channels where small streams meander about the fields before converging and cutting through the shingle bank to the side. The exit also gives the sea access; hence, the channels are estuarine in appearance with muddy edges. In severe storms wave action closes the cut, the channels flood and the marsh becomes a great lake.

The marsh supports quite low numbers of wildfowl and waders (Tables 3 and 4). Formerly Greylag Geese wintered here, but in the mid-1960s they deserted the area in favour of less accessible fields near Broad Lough to the south. Nowadays the marsh has a winter population of **Wigeon, Lapwing, Golden Plover, Curlew, Redshanks** and **Dunlin.** It also attracts rare waders more regularly than most east coast wetlands. But the specialities of the marsh are Bewick's Swans and Little Gulls. Bewick's Swans arrive when there is hard weather in Britain and the marsh floods following a storm. Numbers build up daily until the exit channel is opened and the water level drops. Up to 138 have been counted. Little Gulls occur along the tideline and over the marsh in larger numbers than anywhere else in Ireland, at times in flocks of over 100 birds. Most occur in early spring and late autumn.

In summer some Mallard, Shelduck, Oystercatchers and Redshank nest on or near the marsh and on the shingle beach there is a Little Tern colony.

Broad Lough

Broad Lough is about ten kilometres south of Kilcoole and lies in a similar situation behind the shingle bank. However, there is a much broader expanse of water, though the edge is muddy and estuarine because of the tidal inflow. The Vartry River reaches the sea through Broad Lough after flowing east from Ashford and the Devil's Glen. The lough is long, narrow and very shallow at its southern end; at its northern extremity it broadens out into a reed-fringed lake.

It is clear from Tables 3, 4 and 5 that Broad Lough supports a similar community of wintering birds to the community at Kilcoole. Indeed, the two sites support wintering Wigeon and Teal flocks which interchange between them depending on the level of disturbance. The flocks of Golden Plover and Curlew probably move between the two wetlands very frequently. However, Broad Lough tends to support more ducks than Kilcoole, probably because of the greater area of water and a prohibition on shooting. Whooper and Bewick's Swans are regular in small numbers and up to 70 Greylag Geese, a population of national importance, winter in fields just north of the lake and frequently come to the water.

The lough is an Irish Wildbird Conservancy sanctuary by arrangement with a local landowner and is also protected by a no-shooting Order.

Poulaphouca Reservoir

The reservoir at Poulaphouca (Fig. 4) is the first inland wetland to be dealt with in this chapter. It was constructed in 1938-40 for a hydro-electric scheme and to provide water for Dublin. The valley which was flooded was the ancient bed of a huge lake worked out in pre-glacial times. The lake and its surrounding hills are visually very attractive and the road around the lake is a popular scenic route for Dubliners.

The area is important as one of the largest remaining haunts of Greylag Geese in Ireland. Up to 275, more usually between 150 and 250, spend the winter here. Numbers were lower prior to 1954, only 70-80 wintering, but since then the geese have seemed to thrive. Very often a Pink-footed Goose or two spends the winter with the Greylags. The lake also supports 250-400 Mallard, 100-250 Teal, 200-400 Wigeon, up to 100 Tufted Ducks and up to 170 Pochard in winter.

Part of the lake is protected by a no-shooting Order.

Lough Derravaragh

There are a number of very important lakes in the midlands (Fig. 5). In this chapter they are dealt with in the order of the size of their waterfowl populations. Lough Derravaragh, which holds the largest regular winter population of ducks (Table 7), is a large limestone lake on the River Inny system. Raised bog lies behind the north-west end, but the long arm which runs to the south-east extends between oak-covered limestone ridges. In recent years the drainage of the River Inny has lowered the water level and extensive areas of the lake bed are exposed at the north-west end as sand and mud banks which provide feeding for migrant waders.

The lake's primary importance is as a haunt of diving ducks (Table 6). In early autumn there is a post-breeding congregation of 800-1,000 Mallard which begin to disperse in September when the first regular counts are made. Pochard arrive from mid-August and build up to a September peak of 5,000-6,000 birds before most of them disperse, presumably to smaller lakes nearby. Tufted Duck arrive in mid-October and up to 2,000 occur in winter, but numbers fluctuate considerably due to local movements. An enormous flock of Coots peaks at about 3,000 in November and December. Surprisingly few dabbling ducks spend the winter and geese are rare, but small numbers of Whooper Swans (up to 60) occur. The population of Pochard is of international importance, that of Tufted Ducks of national importance.

In spring and autumn the sandy and muddy shore on the north-west corner attracts a great variety of migrant wader species, many more than have been recorded at any other midland lake.

Table 6

Average numbers of the most common duck species recorded in the peak month at each major wetland in the midlands 1971-72 to 1974-75. Conventions are as in Table 5.

	Lough Derravaragh	Lough Iron	Lough Owel
Mallard	600	1,500	1,100
Teal	200	300	300
Wigeon	100	300	600
Shoveler	—	500	1,300
Tufted Duck	1,900*	500	1,100
Pochard	5,600**	1,300	900

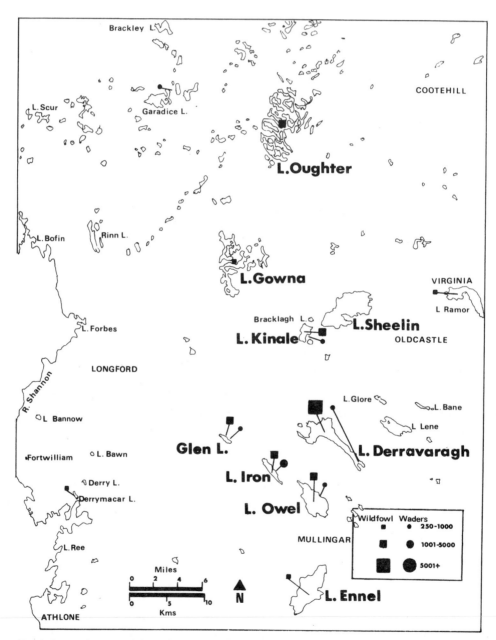

Fig. 5. Principal concentrations of wildfowl and waders in the Midlands

Lough Owel

Lough Owel is another shallow lake on limestone and is important for trout fishing. Its area is slightly smaller than that of Lough Derravaragh (950 hectares against 1,100 hectares) and it lacks the shoreline which provides feeding for shore waders at the larger lake. However, in winter 1972-73 it held larger numbers of ducks than Derravaragh (Table 7).

Like most of the surrounding lakes Owel has a sizeable winter population of Tufted Duck and Pochard (up to 2,000 of each have been recorded, but numbers fluctuate). However, it also holds many more dabbling ducks than any other lake in the vicinity. The concentration of Shoveler, much the largest in Ireland, is of international importance. Counts of 2,000 have been made in November; those birds would represent about 25% of the Irish winter population. Numbers of Mallard, Teal and Wigeon are usually higher than at most of the surrounding wetlands but not exceptional. Yet 2,500 Mallard, 500 Teal and 1,500 Wigeon were counted on 31st January 1973. Weather conditions were not unusually harsh at this time and the reason for the large numbers is not known. Perhaps they were mainly birds from nearby wetlands, for there is considerable movement between Owel and Derravaragh and Iron. Pochard, for example, do not begin to arrive at Owel until October, about the time they are leaving Derragh. Lough Owel also has large numbers of Coots, peaking at 2,500 in mid-winter.

Table 7

Maximum numbers of ducks, geese and swans recorded at midland lakes, 1971-72 to 1974-75 (NC indicates no count).

	1971-72	1972-73	1973-74	1974-75
Lough Owel	4,100	10,800	3,100	2,900
Lough Derravaragh	6,600	9,000	NC	5,900
Lough Iron	1,700	3,000	3,800	2,100
Lough Oughter	2,100	NC	NC	500
Lough Gowna	1,100	700	NC	NC
Lough Ennel	NC	NC	NC	500

Lough Iron

Lough Iron is smaller than Lough Owel and situated about two kilometres to the north-west. It has large wintering populations of Tufted Duck and Pochard, but not so large as those of Derravaragh or Owel. It also has wintering flocks of up to 300 each of Mallard, Teal and Wigeon. Very large numbers of Shoveler sometimes occur when disturbed at Lough Owel. Like Derravaragh this lake has wintering Whooper Swans, though they number up to 100 or so.

The main importance of Lough Iron is its status as one of the very few sites of international importance for the Greenland White-fronted Goose. Up to 200 are regularly reported at the lake, occasionally as many as 250.

Lough Oughter

Lough Oughter is a complicated maze of channels and small lakes formed by the submergence of drumlins in south Cavan by the River Erne (Fig. 5). The southern part of the system is well wooded.

Our knowledge of the waterfowl of this area is based on only two counts carried out in December 1971 and February 1975. A total of 563 Whooper Swans was counted in 1971, but in early 1975 only 26 were found at a time when the lake was extremely flooded. It seems likely that the area usually supports large numbers of Whooper Swans, but that these move off to flooded fields when the water level rises significantly. In January 1967 407 wild swans were counted in this area in an aerial survey (Cabot 1967b) and there have been casual reports of large numbers of wild swans, presumably Whooper. These figures are more than sufficient for the system to qualify as a wetland of international importance. Small numbers of other wildfowl species also occur and Lough Oughter has a winter population of 50-150 Great Crested Grebes.

The area is owned by the state and an annual no-shooting Order is imposed.

Lough Gowna

Lough Gowna is another rather complex lake joined to the River Erne and is divided into two main sections. The lake is at the centre of a coarse fishing area. It is not of great importance for waterfowl in national or international terms but holds a flock of Wigeon (up to 360) and smaller numbers of Tufted Ducks, Pochard and Goldeneye.

Lough Ennel

Lough Ennel is a large, shallow lake on limestone situated south of Lough Owel in Westmeath (Fig. 5). The only count during the years from 1971-72 to 1974-75 was in February 1975 when the water level was high and the main waterfowl species present was the Tufted Duck, of which 465 were counted. Prior to the present survey, counts in January 1969 and 1970 produced totals of 900-1,250 Tufted Ducks, 300-800 Pochard and up to 1,200 Coots. Like most of the lakes in this area Lough Ennel requires more study.

A flock of up to 100 White-fronted Geese winters in the area. This flock is separate from that which winters at Lough Iron.

Lough Kinale

This is a small lake adjoining the heavily polluted Lough Sheelin, once famous for its trout angling. The area of the lake is only 388 hectares. It is surrounded by low-lying wet pasture and large reed beds fringe the margin.

The value of Lough Kinale for wildfowl is far from properly understood. In January 1969, 2,160 Tufted Duck and 2,425 Pochard were counted, but subsequent counts in November 1970, October 1974, November 1974, February 1975 and September 1975 have produced much smaller totals. The largest count since 1969 was in November 1970 when 258 Tufted Duck and 233 Pochard were counted, together with smaller numbers of other species. In February 1975 a huge raft of Coots was present, the total being estimated at 2,400.

Glen Lough

Glen Lough is situated about five kilometres north-west of Lough Iron (Fig. 5). Unlike most of the other lakes in the midlands it does not have a significant diving duck population. Instead it holds large numbers of dabbling ducks. Very few counts have been made but 200 Mallard, 1,000 Teal and 700 Wigeon have been recorded and White-fronted Geese, probably from the Lough Iron population, are regular visitors.

Thurles Sugar Factory Lagoon

Right on the southern border of the midland region discussed in this chapter is situated one of the best wetlands in Tipperary, the lagoon near the Thurles Sugar Factory, about four kilometres south-south-west of the town. The area has long been known to hold large numbers of ducks and some wild swans but because of the extent of vegetation it is very difficult to count. In December 1972 and January 1973 several visits were paid to the area and the number of ducks estimated at 1,000 or more. The individual species were not counted, but Teal, Wigeon, Shoveler and Pintail were all present and in that order of abundance. Nearly 40 Whooper and 120 Bewick's Swans were also counted.

More information is needed on this wetland.

SOUTH

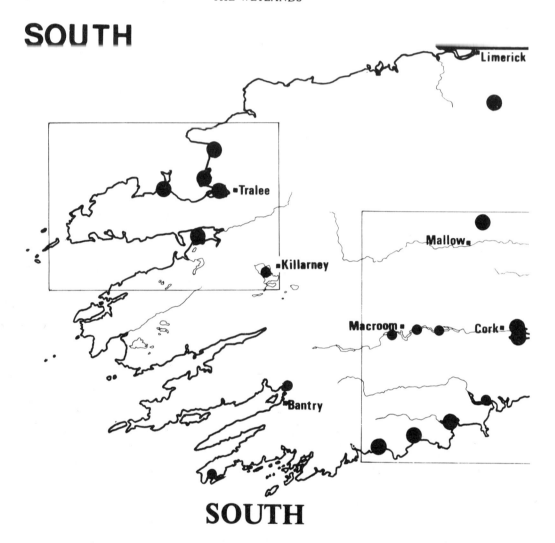

SOUTH

The majority of the most important wetlands south of a line drawn from Limerick to the Wicklow/Wexford border are estuaries, bays and brackish lagoons on the coast. This area, which includes the counties of Wexford, Waterford, Cork, Kerry, Limerick and the southern halves of Tipperary, Kilkenny and Carlow, is south of the region of extensive raised bogs in the central lowlands where most of Ireland's most important inland wetlands are located. Over much of the region the land is good for farming: the lowland areas of Waterford, east and north Cork, Limerick, south Tipperary, south Kilkenny, Wexford and south Carlow have very few wetlands of value for birds. West Cork and Kerry are mountainous regions with exposed coasts, high winds and heavy rain and a similar scarcity of inland wetlands.

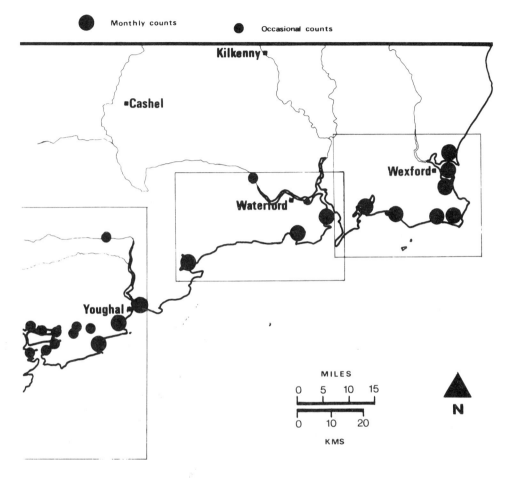

Fig. 6. *Extent of coverage at wetlands in the South*

There are mountains elsewhere in the area: a broken line of mountains stretches south-west from the Wicklow Mountains across the centre of the region as far as the Cork and Kerry sandstones. They include the granite Blackstairs Mountains and the old red sandstone Comeraghs, Knockmealdowns and Kilworths. Farther north are the isolated Galtee, Slievenaman, Slievenamuck and Slieve Ardagh ranges. The rivers which drain the area flood the surrounding valleys less frequently than those of the midlands and west. The most important wetlands associated with the rivers are the artificial reservoirs on the Lee, the marshes and fields by the Suir near Coolfin and the fields by the Blackwater near Lismore. Otherwise, there are very few inland wetlands apart from the acidic mountain lakes and the more productive ones are treated individually below.

The coastline is varied. On the eastern edge of the area the low-lying Dublin and Wicklow coastline continues unbroken by any major estuary as far as the mouth of the Slaney at Wexford Harbour. The south coast is utterly different. From Carnsore Point in Wexford a series of estuaries and brackish lagoons breaks the line of the coast as far as Rosscarbery in west Cork. Almost all are important for waterfowl. From Rosscarbery west and round to the mouth of the Shannon the main features are the enormous rias which divide the south-west corner of Ireland into great fingers. Most of these are deep and contain few wildfowl or waders, but Castlemaine Harbour and Tralee Bay are striking exceptions with extensive inter-tidal sand-banks, mudflats and salt marshes. These two bays and the associated lagoons of north-west Kerry (Fig. 10), together with the south coast estuaries, form the most important groups of wetlands in the region.

The threats to these sites include the two common to most Irish estuaries: the spread of *Spartina* and industrial development. *Spartina* is present on most of the estuaries, but has encroached most seriously at Tramore Bay and, especially, Cork Harbour. Unfortunately, pressure to reclaim mudflat for the location of new industry is also greatest in Cork Harbour, though it must be a potential threat at Wexford and Waterford Harbours as well. A particular problem on this coast is the instability of the brackish lagoons contained behind sand and shingle banks. Some, such as Tacumshin in Wexford, are being drained by man; others, such as Ballycotton in Cork, are becoming fresh-water lakes as the outlets to the sea are blocked by debris following the more frequent south-easterly storms of the past few years.

The birds of the coastal counties are well known. Those occurring at the main wetlands in Wexford have recently been summarised in an attractive guide to the best places to watch birds in the county (Merne 1975). The status of birds in Limerick has also been set out in a booklet (Stapleton 1975). In addition, a bird report is published annually in Cork, biennially in Waterford and one was produced for Wexford in 1970 and 1971. The birds of Kerry are well watched by a group of observers in Tralee, though their observations are not published in any local report.

The most abundant wildfowl in the area are undoubtedly Wigeon (15,000-20,000) which are present on every estuary. The commonest waders are Lapwing and Golden Plover which can number well over 10,000 each in Wexford Harbour, Ballymacoda Bay and Cork Harbour, but they move inland frequently and we have little idea of the true numbers on the coast at any time of the winter. The next most common wader is the Dunlin. Up to 35,000 winter in the area. But the most characteristic birds of the estuaries are the Black-tailed Godwits which number in the region of 8,000 birds.

Very few counts of gulls have been made. The largest concentrations are probably in Cork Harbour where they feed on refuse and effluent. Divers winter off the coast and in most of the bays. Great Crested Grebes winter in Wexford Harbour and Cork Harbour but are very rare in west Cork and Kerry. In summer there was a large tern colony in Wexford Harbour up to 1975 and Mallard, Shelduck, Lapwing and Ringed Plover breed along most of the coastline, including the main wetlands. Oystercatchers breed on the Wexford and east Waterford coast and in west Cork and Kerry. Redshanks nest in Wexford.

In the remainder of this chapter the wetlands are dealt with in county order, working from east to west around the coast.

Wexford Harbour and Slobs

Wexford Harbour is the estuary of the Slaney river (Fig. 7). North and south of the broad estuary are the slobs: areas of alluvial mud which were reclaimed in the mid-nineteenth century. The North Slob consists of 1,000 hectares of well drained land, considerably less than half of which is pasture. The remainder is under arable crops, but this has only been the case since the land was drained more efficiently following consolidation of a number of holdings into one farm in the early 1960s. Formerly the land was poorly drained and largely pasture. The South Slob, on the south side of the harbour, is slightly smaller and was reclaimed shortly after the North Slob. The main crop is good quality grass which is cut several times a year, dried and compressed into grass meal pellets. Barley, wheat and sugar beet are also grown.

Both slobs are criss-crossed by drainage ditches and have a broad, shallow channel running through them.

Out in the harbour itself most of the inter-tidal mudflats are on the southern side. The main wader roosts are at Rosslare Point and Tern Island, a small and very unstable sandy island near the mouth of the harbour.

The area is unquestionably the most important wildfowl haunt in Ireland, supporting up to 15,400 birds in winter (Table 9). Nearly half the world population of the Greenland White-fronted Goose (over 5,000 birds) spend the winter in the area, feeding on the slobs and flighting out at dusk to roost on Tern Island and other sand banks in the harbour. The first Greenland White-fronted Geese appear to have come to the slobs during the second decade of this century, but numbers were low and the present numbers were not reached until the late 1940s. Interestingly, they seem to have replaced the Greylag Geese which were abundant up to the 1940s and are now very rare on the slobs. The Greylag Goose decline here, as elsewhere in Ireland, is believed to have been due to an increase in food supply in Scotland in post-war years. Brent Geese winter in the harbour in numbers of international significance (Table 8) and have begun to feed on pasture on the slobs since spring 1974. Small numbers of Pink-footed, Canada and Barnacle Geese also occur annually and a blue phase Snow Goose in most years. The slobs are also of international importance for Pintail and Bewick's Swans (Table 8). The latter species was traditionally more regular than the Whooper Swan but numbers have increased greatly in recent years. The swans feed on potato fields on the North Slob and on grass on the South Slob as well as on stubble and sugar beet on both slobs. Mallard occur on the slobs in autumn in numbers of national importance: this is the largest concentration in the Republic. Scaup winter in Wexford Harbour in numbers up to 500 at times, but they are far from as numerous as in the early 1960s when up to 3,000 wintered.

The area also holds the largest wader populations in Wexford (Table 10). In 1973-74 the numbers were boosted by an exceptional count of 22,000 Lapwings on the slobs. It is clear that the slobs act as a refuge in hard weather for Lapwing and Golden Plover driven west from Britain. The winter population of Black-tailed Godwits is of international importance and the populations of Grey Plover, Bar-tailed Godwits and Redshanks of national importance. The diversity of habitat within the area — ranging from mudflats to brackish channels on the slobs — attracts a number of scarcer wader species. The largest concentrations of Spotted Redshanks in Ireland (up to 100 in autumn) occur on the slobs, for example.

In summer parties of Little Gulls are annual at the slobs. The slobs are also an important breeding area for Mallard and small numbers of Shoveler, Tufted Duck and Shelduck also nest. Out in the harbour Tern Island holds the largest tern colony in Ireland and the largest colony of Roseate Terns in Europe. Numbers have declined, however, in the past decade as the island has been eroded.

The main potential threat to the area is of a change in agricultural practice on the slobs which might not coincide with the welfare of the waterfowl. There is also the possibility of industrial development because of the close proximity of the port of Wexford. Only three areas are specifically protected — (1) 100 hectares of the North Slob owned and 50 hectares leased jointly by the Forest and Wildlife Service and the Irish Wildbird Conservancy; (2) Tern Island and (3) Rosslare Point which are Irish Wildbird Conservancy sanctuaries.

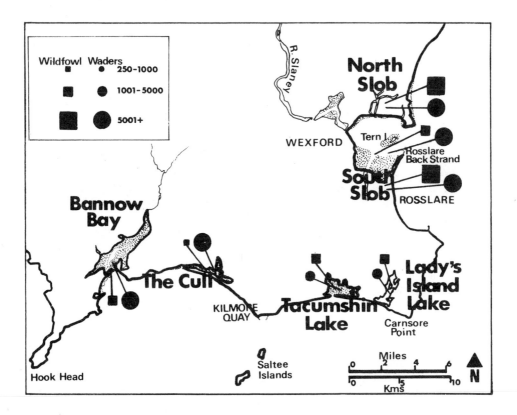

Fig. 7. Principal concentrations of wildfowl and waders in Wexford

Pump house and wildfowl collection at the North Slob

Lady's Island Lake

Lady's Island Lake is a 466 hectare lagoon impounded behind a shingle bank built up by the dominant wave action from the south-south-east, like Tacumshin Lake four kilometres to the west (Fig. 7). Lady's Island Lake has been impounded much longer, however, for the exit is blocked and inundation from the sea is rare. Each spring a drainage channel is cut through the shingle bank to lower the water level. The lake is shallow and a large area of sand and mud is exposed at the northern end of the lake for some time after the channel is opened.

As will be seen from Table 9 Lady's Island Lake held a minimum of 7,000 wildfowl in 1971-72, but no more than 1,800 in the following winters. This should be taken into account in examining the average figures at Table 8. In 1971-72 there were maxima of 2,728 Wigeon, 700 Tufted Duck, 1,850 Pochard, 595 Mute Swans and 268 Bewick's Swans as well as 2,850 Coots which are not included in the wildfowl total. Since then the peak counts have been 520 Wigeon, 934 Tufted Duck, 370 Pochard, 104 Mute Swans, 35 Bewick's Swans and 960 Coots. Counts in November, January and February in 1969-70 and 1970-71 gave somewhat lower totals than in 1971-72 but still far greater than in subsequent years. The high numbers in 1971-72 were due to an abnormal abundance of *Potomageton* (O. J. Merne *in litt.*).

In autumn, when the water level is reasonably low, a wide variety of wader species may be seen. Curlew Sandpipers and vagrants from North America are annual.

Table 8

Average numbers of the most common species recorded in the peak month at each major Wexford wetland, 1971-72 to 1974-75. Conventions are as in Table 5.

	Wexford Harbour and Slobs	Lady's Island Lake	Tacum-shin	The Cull	Bannow Bay
Mallard	2,500*	—	200	—	100
Teal	1,300	100	100	200	100
Wigeon	1,600	900	800	300	800
Pintail	900**	100	—	—	100
Shoveler	100	100	—	—	—
Scaup	300*	—	200*	—	—
Tufted Duck	200	800	100	—	—
Pochard	100	900	100	—	—
Shelduck	200	—	—	—	300
White-fronted Goose	5,200**	—	—	—	—
Brent Goose	400**	—	500**	100	300**
Bewick's Swan	200**	100**	—	—	—
Oystercatcher	1,600	—	100	100	500
Lapwing	4,800	400	900	2,100	3,200
Grey Plover	100*	—	—	—	100*
Golden Plover	6,800	400	600	2,600	4,800
Curlew	1,000	100	600	400	1,300
Black-tailed Godwit	1,200**	—	100	200	200
Bar-tailed Godwit	800*	—	200	100	600
Redshank	700*	—	—	400	800*
Knot	100	—	—	200	300*
Dunlin	3,000	100	900	600	2,100

Tacumshin Lake

Tacumshin is another lagoon which has developed behind a sand spit (Fig. 7). The area of the lagoon is 464 hectares, similar to that of Lady's Island Lake, but, unlike that lake, Tacumshin was tidal until 1974 when the exit was blocked and a drainage pipe placed through the shingle bar. In summer the water area is now reduced to about 100 hectares. A narrow channel at the western end of the sand spit up to 1974 allowed the tide to flow in and out, but was periodically blocked by shifting sand. At low water quite an extensive area of mudflat was exposed.

Since the decline in the number of wildfowl wintering at Lady's Island Lake this area has come to support the second largest population of wildfowl in Wexford (Table 9). The area is of international importance as a wintering site for Brent Geese and of national importance for Scaup (Table 8). It also holds over 100 Bewick's Swans on occasion, almost certainly birds which have come from the Wexford Slobs. The geese and dabbling ducks feed on the salt marsh of the islands at the western end of the lake.

Table 9

Maximum numbers of ducks, geese and swans recorded at Wexford wetlands, 1971-72 to 1974-75

	1971-72	1972-73	1973-74	1974-75
Wexford Harbour and Slobs	15,400	15,100	15,400	14,100
Lady's Island Lake	7,000	1,800	1,700	1,800
Tacumshin	2,100	2,000	3,500	2,800
Bannow Bay	1,700	2,100	2,100	1,800
The Cull	800	700	700	900

Most of the waders which occur at the lake feed on the mudflats around these islands, though Ruffs prefer the White Hole, a brackish marsh at the north-western end of the lake. The only known breeding record of Avocets in Ireland took place here in 1938 when two pairs nested.

Parties of Little Gulls are regular in June and large concentrations of Lesser Black-backed Gulls (up to 600) occur in autumn.

There is some danger that the area may be totally drained by artificial channels cut through the sand spit.

The Cull

The Cull is a long, narrow estuary which runs parallel to the coast behind a ridge of high sand-dunes (Fig. 7). The eastern half of the estuary was reclaimed within the last hundred years, following the construction of The Cull Bank. This part of the estuary once held large numbers of ducks and a flock of over 200 White-fronted Geese. Since the completion of a more efficient drainage scheme in the 1950s few birds occur at this end.

Just west of The Cull Bank is a small island which provides roosting security for waders at high tide. This area holds flocks of several thousand Lapwing and Golden Plover and smaller numbers of other wader species (Table 8). The number of ducks occurring here is very low. Occasionally, small parties of White-fronted Geese pay a brief visit.

Bannow Bay

Bannow Bay is a large tidal bay situated just east of Hook Head (Fig. 7). The entrance is narrow due to the encroachment of a sand spit on the west side. The bay is fed by the Owenduff and Corock rivers and a number of small streams. At low tide a large expanse of mudflat is exposed. Salt marsh at Clonmines at the north end of the bay and at the mouth of the bay provide roosting areas for the birds which feed on the mud. Like Wexford Harbour and Tacumshin nearby, Bannow Bay has an internationally important flock of Brent Geese (Table 8). It also has the largest concentration of Shelduck in Wexford. But it ranks only fourth in Co. Wexford in terms of the total number of wildfowl counted each winter (Table 9). As a wader haunt

Table 10

Maximum numbers of waders recorded at Wexford wetlands, 1971-72 to 1974-75 (NC indicates no count).

	1971-72	1972-73	1973-74	1974-75
Wexford Harbour and Slobs	NC	20,500	41,800	18,100
Bannow Bay	10,400	13,900	18,800	19,500
The Cull	5,100	5,600	10,800	8,000
Tacumshin	3,000	2,700	3,400	4,700
Lady's Island Lake	500	1,800	500	2,600

it ranks much higher — second only to Wexford Harbour (Table 10) and indeed in winter 1974-75 ranked ahead of Wexford Harbour. The most numerous species are Lapwing, Golden Plover and Dunlin, all of which number over 2,000 and the first two species frequently well in excess of this. The bay also holds nationally important concentrations of Redshanks and Knot.

There have been some proposals to reclaim the entire bay.

Table 11

Average numbers of the most common species recorded in the peak month at each major Waterford wetland, 1971-72 to 1974-75. Conventions are as in Table 5.

	Waterford Harbour	Tramore Bay	Dungarvan Harbour	Kinsale-beg	Coolfin Marshes	Blackwater near Lismore
Mallard	—	100	—	—	—	100
Teal	—	—	100	100	100	200
Wigeon	—	1,500	600	700	100	1,000
Shelduck	—	100	300	100	—	—
Greylag Goose	—	—	—	—	100*	—
Brent Goose	—	200	200	—	—	—
Bewick's Swan	—	—	—	—	—	100**
Oystercatcher	400	400	800	200	—	—
Lapwing	200	200	400	700	—	1,200
Grey Plover	—	200*	100*	—	—	—
Golden Plover	500	700	1,500	100	100	—
Curlew	200	300	400	200	—	500
Black-tailed Godwit	100	100	900**	—	—	1,300**
Bar-tailed Godwit	300	300	500	100	—	—
Redshank	200	300	400	200	—	—
Knot	400*	200	1,900*	—	—	—
Dunlin	700	1,500	1,500	1,400	—	—

Waterford Harbour

During the years of this survey the entire shore of Waterford Harbour was censused on only one occasion, in January 1971. But counts have been carried out on the west shore each winter month over the four years. The harbour is a long and rather deep estuary, fed by the river Barrow and most of the available sand and mud is on the west shore (Fig. 8). Those who counted the entire estuary in January 1971 located only a very few additional shore waders, but they did find nearly 2,000 Lapwing and 7,000 Golden Plover.

The harbour is not of any importance for ducks but it holds medium sized flocks of the locally common wader species (Table 11).

Tramore Bay

Tramore Bay exhibits yet again the formation of a lagoon impounded behind sand dunes so common on the south coast, but the Back Strand, as it is known, is at an earlier stage of development than either Lady's Island Lake or Tacumshin in Wexford (Fig. 8). The inner bay has extensive intertidal mudflats and, on the south side, a salt marsh and a large expanse of *Spartina*. Tidal scour is still quite effective and the entrance to the inner bay is never closed.

Tramore Back Strand holds the largest gathering of wildfowl in Waterford (Table 12). The great majority are Wigeon, but there are small winter populations of Mallard, Shelduck and Brent Geese (Table 11). It ranks second to Dungarvan Harbour in terms of the number of waders occurring in the area (Table 13), but the spring peak of *c.* 200 Grey Plover is one of the largest in Ireland.

Spartina has spread over much of the salt marsh and some of the mudflat, but the main inter-tidal zone is still clear. There are no other known threats to the area.

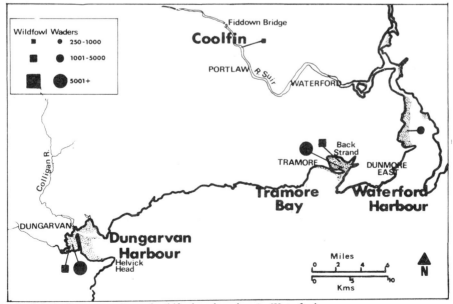

Fig. 8. Principal concentrations of wildfowl and waders in Waterford

Dungarvan Harbour

Dungarvan Harbour is a large circular east-facing bay, the inner part of which is enclosed by a sand spit called the Cunnigar (Fig. 8). The inner harbour is an inter-tidal mudflat, fringed with salt marsh on the south and south-west sides and along the edge of the Cunnigar. East of the Cunnigar there is an extensive area of inter-tidal sand where *Zostera* or eel-grass, the main food of Brent Geese, grows extensively (Guiry and Kilty 1972).

The bay ranks second to Tramore Bay in the county for the number of wildfowl recorded (Table 12), Wigeon, Shelduck and Brent Geese being the most numerous (Table 11). This is the most westerly bay between Wexford and west Kerry in which Brent Geese winter. As a wader haunt it is much the most important in Waterford, holding internationally important numbers of Black-tailed Godwits and nationally important numbers of Grey Plover and Knot. The sandy beach east of the Cunnigar provides cockles and lugworms respectively for the largest flocks of Oystercatchers and Bar-tailed Godwits in the county.

Spartina also occurs in this bay, but the rate of spread does not appear to be as great as at Tramore.

Table 12

Maximum number of ducks, geese and swans recorded at Waterford estuaries, 1971-72 to 1974-75 (NC indicates no count).

	1971-72	1972-73	1973-74	1974-75
Tramore Bay	1,700	2,500	2,100	1,200
Dungarvan Harbour	1,600	1,800	1,400	1,500
Kinsalebeg	NC	NC	NC	900
Waterford Harbour (west)	100	100	200	100

Kinsalebeg

Kinsalebeg is a small muddy inlet on the eastern side of Youghal Bay (Fig. 9). At high tide most of the birds in Youghal Bay roost at Kinsalebeg; at low tide some of the waders move out over the sand and mud of the main bay. Wigeon (up to 700) and Dunlin (up to 1,400) are the most numerous species but most of the locally common waders are also to be found in smaller numbers.

Table 13

Maximum number of waders recorded at Waterford estuaries, 1971-72 to 1974-75 (NC indicates no count).

	1971-72	1972-73	1973-74	1974-75
Dungarvan Harbour	8,100	8,700	11,000	9,600
Tramore Bay	5,100	7,600	8,200	5,300
Waterford Harbour (west)	2,900	4,400	3,900	5,400
Kinsalebeg	NC	NC	NC	2,900

Coolfin Marshes

The marshes at Coolfin, between Portlaw and Fiddown Bridge on the River Suir (Fig. 8) are of importance because of the wintering population of Greylag Geese. Up to 150 Greylags have been counted here and small numbers of ducks also occur.

The area is protected by an annual no-shooting Order.

River Blackwater near Lismore

The flooded callows on the edge of the river Blackwater between Lismore and Ballyduff support internationally important populations of Bewick's Swans and Black-tailed Godwits (Table 11). The birds recorded here are reminiscent of those to be seen on the River Shannon in the midlands — large numbers of Wigeon, smaller numbers of Mallard, Teal and Bewick's Swans, and large numbers of Lapwing, Curlew and Black-tailed Godwits. More observations are required to assess the precise importance of the area. In particular, we need to know the relationship between the number of birds and the water-level on the Blackwater, but the area appears to be of very little value when the callows are not flooded.

Ballymacoda

Ballymacoda is the estuary of the small Womanagh river (Fig. 9). It is a 600 hectare expanse of marshy fields, salt marsh and mudflats which have been remarkably little worked apart from the ornithological studies which form the basis of this summary. The area must be extremely rich to support the enormous numbers of waders which use the estuary.

The estuary has a flock of *c.* 1,000 Wigeon and small numbers of Mallard, Teal and Shelduck, but its wader numbers place it among the most important Irish wetlands (Table 16). The regular presence of one of the largest flocks of Golden Plover in the country (up to 13,000 have been counted) and large numbers of Lapwing (up to 8,000) should, however, be considered when comparing the maximum numbers of waders each year with other estuaries. These birds feed on farmland and only use the estuary as a roost. The Lapwing feed on grass, stubble and beet fields. Smiddy (1977) has studied the feeding behaviour of all the waders and he noted that over half the winter population of Oystercatchers and Redshanks feed on the same fields as the Lapwing. The entire Black-tailed Godwit flock sometimes feeds in fields and in exceptionally wet conditions up to 500 Dunlin do so as well.

The number of waders using the area qualifies Ballymacoda as a site of international importance for these birds and the Black-tailed Godwit flock alone is also of international significance.

There are no protective measures and there is presently no known threat to the estuary.

Ballycotton

The wetlands at Ballycotton consist of a shallow, brackish lagoon behind a shingle bank, three smaller, muddy pools, reed-beds and an extensive inter-tidal sandy beach. The main lagoon was an inlet of the sea until the 1930s when it was cut off by the development of the shingle bank, in effect a storm beach. At present the lagoon is totally impounded. The exit channel is periodically excavated but in south-easterly winds shifting sand, shingle and seaweed are swept across the mouth of the channel blocking it completely.

As may be seen from Table 14 the area holds small populations of Mallard, Teal, Wigeon, Pochard, Shelduck and the common wader species. Up to 1973-74 the larger lake had a wintering population of up to 50 Gadwall, over 10% of the Irish population. Since the water level of the lake has risen following the closure of the exit channel these birds have dispersed to several nearby lakes, including Lough Aderry and Ballyhonock Lake (Fig. 9), but when the channel is dug out and the level drops some of the Gadwall return. The area is important, however, not primarily for the numbers of ducks and waders occurring there but for the diversity of species. Scarce wildfowl and waders from Europe and, more particularly, North America are more frequently seen there than at any other Irish wetland with the exception of Akeragh Lough in Kerry.

The area is subject to two major threats. Planning applications for tourist developments continue to arise and are fought by the conservation organisations. But the main threat is posed by the closure of the exit channel from the lake, the increase in water-level, the associated loss of muddy shoreline and the rapid spread of *Phragmites*.

Most of the area is the subject of an annual no-shooting Order.

Bellycotton lake (foreground) and the smaller Shanagarry pools (top right hand corner) at high tide.

Table 14

Average numbers of the most common species recorded in the peak month at selected Cork wetlands, 1971-72 to 1974-75. Conventions are as in Table 5. The figures for Cork Harbour are based on only one count, made in December 1974.

	Bally-macoda	Bally-cotton	Cork Har-bour	Court-mac-sherry	Clona-kilty Bay	Ross-car-bery	Kilcol-man
Mallard	100	200	300	100	100	—	300
Teal	200	200	1,400	—	100	—	500
Wigeon	1,000	400	1,800	100	500	—	400
Pintail	—	—	100	—	—	—	—
Pochard	—	100	—	—	—	—	—
Shelduck	100	100	800*	100	100	—	—
Oystercatcher	300	100	1,600*	300	200	100	—
Lapwing	4,000	800	6,400	700	1,200	100	200
Grey Plover	—	—	100	—	—	—	—
Golden Plover	9,500	1,000	5,300	2,200	1,500	200	—
Curlew	1,300	400	1,000	100	800	300	—
Black-t Godwit	800**	100	3,600**	100	500	100	—
Bar-t Godwit	400	100	500	500	300	—	—
Redshank	300	—	1,000*	200	300	100	—
Knot	100	—	400	—	200	—	—
Dunlin	4,200	300	7,700*	200	1,100	100	—

Cork Harbour

Cork Harbour consists of two large areas of open water — Lough Mahon and Cobh Harbour — on a limestone basin, separated from each other and from the sea by ridges of Old Red Sandstone. Channels cut deeply through the sandstone by the River Lee at the western side and the Owenacurra at the eastern side connect Lough Mahon and its extension to the east, known as the 'North Channel', to Cobh Harbour and the open sea.

The harbour is an extremely difficult area to count. Inter-tidal mudflat is distributed around almost the entire area and there are high tide roosts at Lough Beg, Douglas, Tivoli, several places along the North Channel and at Whitegate (Fig. 9). Although individual sections have been well studied, the only complete counts of the harbour have been in March 1968 (wildfowl only), December 1974 and December 1976, though the north and east coasts from Douglas to Whitegate where most of the birds are found were also counted in January 1969, 1971 and 1976. It is rather disappointing that so few counts have been made of the birds of this harbour where the pressure of industrial development is greater than at any other Irish wetland.

Cork Harbour is the most important wetland in Co. Cork for wildfowl and shore waders. Only the exceptional numbers of Lapwing and Golden Plover at Ballymacoda in 1972-73 place that estuary ahead of Cork Harbour in Table 16. The area holds

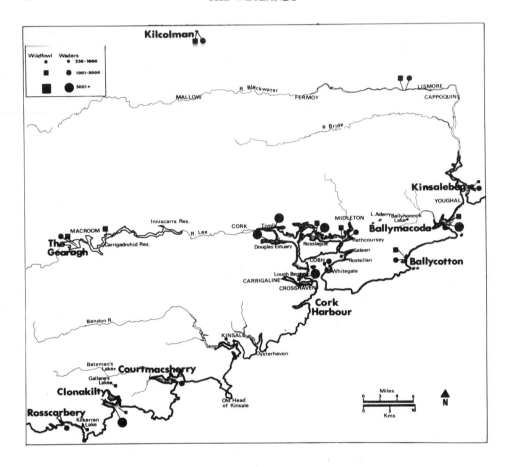

Fig. 9. Principal concentrations of wildfowl and waders in Cork

several hundred Mallard, up to 1,400 Teal and 1,800 Wigeon (the highest counts of these species made in the harbour to date) and 70 Pintail as well as the largest concentration of Shelduck in the country (Table 14). The number of Shelduck in the harbour appears to have declined. In March 1968, 2,400 were counted; in January 1969 the count in the North Channel was 1,470 and 1,190 in January 1971. There was some evidence of an increase again in December 1976 when 1,060 were counted. Most of the ducks are found on the North Channel between Tivoli and Rathcoursey with smaller numbers at Rostellan, Whitegate and Lough Beg (Fig. 9). Wild geese are exceptionally rare in the harbour and wild swans occur mainly at the small lake at Rostellan, and then only in small numbers.

Table 15

Maximum numbers of ducks, geese and swans recorded at selected Cork wetlands 1971-72 to 1974-75
(NC indicates no count). Only one count was carried out at Cork Harbour.

	1971-72	1972-73	1973-74	1974-75
Cork Harbour	NC	NC	NC	4,600
Kilcolman	500	900	2,800	1,400
Ballycotton	1,400	1,400	1,600	2,100
Ballymacoda	500	1,700	2,000	1,200
Clonakilty Bay	700	500	700	500
Courtmacsherry Bay	200	100	NC	NC
Rosscarbery	—	100	—	—

The most numerous waders in the harbour are Dunlin. Up to 14,000 have been counted in winter and they are widely dispersed, with the main concentrations of up to 5,000 each in the Lough Mahon and Rosslague areas. Lapwing and Golden Plover are the next most abundant, but these birds feed mainly on the surrounding farmland and use the estuary for roosting.

In autumn several thousand Oystercatchers occur on passage; the largest roost is at Tivoli on the reclaimed mudflats. Probably more than 2,000 Redshanks also occur in autumn. Long lines of them may be seen all round the harbour in September. They are much less noticeable in December when c. 1,000 are present. Both the Oystercatcher and Redshank populations are of national importance. From a European point of view Cork Harbour is probably most important for its winter flock of Black-tailed Godwits. Numbers fluctuate somewhat and the count of 3,500 in December 1974 (Table 14) was a high one, but over 1,500 are invariably present in winter.

The waders are more widely dispersed around the harbour than the wildfowl. The largest concentrations are at Lough Beg, Douglas, Tivoli and the Lough Mahon area and off Rosslague. Cork Harbour also has what must be the biggest gull population on the south coast. The presence of large refuse dumps and sewage outlets provides easy feeding for these birds.

Industrial development threatens the future of Cork Harbour as an important wetland for birds, but it must be remembered that waterfowl can tolerate industry provided they have unpolluted mudflats on which to feed and secure high tide roosts. The Industrial Development Authority owns large tracts of land at Little Island, east of Tivoli, and at Ringaskiddy, north of Lough Beg, and Lough Beg itself. Industrial development in these areas can be compatible with the requirements of the waterfowl but only if carefully planned.

Spartina is also present in Cork Harbour. North of Rosslague, it covers well over half of what was once a large area of mudflat exposed at low tide.

There are no protective measures at all in force for the birds of the area.

Table 16

Maximum numbers of waders recorded at selected Cork wetlands, 1971-72 to 1974-75 (NC indicates no count). Only one count was carried out at Cork Harbour.

	1971-72	1972-73	1973-74	1974-75
Ballymacoda	14,900	29,800	18,400	21,900
Cork Harbour	NC	NC	NC	27,700
Clonakilty Bay	10,500	4,000	5,200	2,300
Ballycotton	3,800	4,500	3,600	4,800
Courtmacsherry Bay	4,400	700	NC	NC
Kilcolman	500	900	2,800	1,400
Rosscarbery	1,400	600	500	400

Courtmacsherry Bay

West of Cork Harbour are a number of inlets, the most significant for birds being Courtmacsherry Bay, Clonakilty Bay and Rosscarbery (Fig. 9). The rather limited areas of inter-tidal mud at Oysterhaven and Kinsale hold relatively few birds. Courtmacsherry is a wide bay of Carboniferous Slate. The outer reaches of the bay are sandy; the inner estuary into which the Arigideen river feeds is muddy. There are very small areas of salt marsh at the head of the estuary and on the south-west side.

The bay holds small populations of ducks, mainly Mallard, Wigeon and Shelduck (Table 14), but a flock of up to 25 Pintail is the only party in Cork beside that in Cork Harbour. Teal are very scarce. The waders are those found on most of the other south coast estuaries but the numbers are relatively small. The channel off the town of Courtmacsherry is frequented by Great Northern and Red-throated Divers throughout the winter, as well as Red-breasted Mergansers and, in most winters, a few Long-tailed Ducks.

Spartina is present on the south-west side of the inlet.

Clonakilty Bay

Clonakilty Bay resembles Courtmacsherry in having estuarine mudflat at the head of a wide, sandy bay. Unlike Courtmacsherry, however, Clonakilty has twin, narrow, muddy inlets at its head and several brackish pools on the edge of marshy fields (Fig. 9).

The number of birds using the estuary is higher than at Courtmacsherry and the area ranks third in the county for the number of waders recorded (Table 16). It is less important for ducks (Table 15) but does have a flock of 500 Wigeon.

Apart from a wintering flock of Black-tailed Godwits which at times numbers up to 700 birds the waders are those species which are common on most Irish estuaries (Table 14). The pools at the head of both inlets offer a different habitat which attracts scarcer European waders in autumn and, in most years, a vagrant or two from North America.

There is a large heronry in trees beside the estuary just below Clonakilty town. A total of 36 nests were occupied in 1975, but only 28 in 1976. The decrease has been ascribed to the closure of the town dump nearby at which many of the Herons scavenged.

Rosscarbery

Rosscarbery is another inlet, west of Clonakilty, but much smaller and with a relatively deep lagoon behind a causeway (Fig. 9). The area of mudflat is quite small and the number of birds recorded is correspondingly low (Tables 15 and 16). Ducks are few and the wader flocks, which include most common species, are quite small.

Kilcolman

North of the Blackwater river the limestone marsh at Kilcolman, popularly known as Kilcolman Bog, is being developed as a wildfowl refuge. The area was once a large lake but has dried out considerably within the past fifty years.

The marsh is currently managed by Mr. and Mrs. R. H. Ridgway, who own part of the marsh, to maximise wildfowl numbers. As may be seen from Table 15 this has been most successful. Maxima of 620 Mallard, 1,200 Teal, 800 Wigeon and 300-400 Shoveler have been recorded, but White-fronted Geese, which once wintered in the area, are now rarely seen.

The area is a joint Eurel/Irish Wildbird Conservancy reserve and shooting is prohibited under a no-shooting Order.

Mrs. R. H. Ridgway feeding Mute and Whooper Swans at Kilcolman

The Gearagh

The Gearagh is the most westerly of the valleys flooded by the Electricity Supply Board in the 1950s when dams were constructed on the river Lee for the siting of hydro-electric generating stations. Prior to the raising of the water level about 1955 the Gearagh was unique in these islands as an example of the type of woodland which prevailed in Ireland 8,000 years ago (Mitchell 1976) — wooded islands separated by numerous narrow channels. Unfortunately, there is no information available on the birds of the area prior to flooding.

Nowadays the Gearagh is a broad lake marked by a forest of blackened tree stumps. It holds a variable population of wildfowl. Maxima of 700 Mallard, 600 Teal, 800 Wigeon and 300 Mute Swans have been recorded. Flocks of Lapwing and Golden Plover together with small numbers of Dunlin are usually present.

Castlemaine Harbour

Castlemaine Harbour is the estuary of the Rivers Maine and Laune at the head of a huge bay (Fig. 10). A series of interlocking sand and shingle spits has formed and salt marsh has developed behind them. There are also extensive mudflats. *Zostera*, the main food of the Brent Goose, grows in a huge bed in the north-east corner, behind the sand-spit at Inch. In the eastern part of the harbour there are reed beds along the edge of the channels; behind the reed beds there is poorly drained agricultural land.

Because the area is so enormous — almost 10,000 hectares — it is extremely difficult to count. Ground counts were made in the winter months during 1972-73 and aerial counts occasionally during 1973-74 and 1974-75, but there were indications that many birds were missed from the air.

As a haunt of wildfowl Castlemaine Harbour is enormously important. Maxima of 1,460 Mallard, 2,000 Teal, 6,800 Wigeon, 2,000 Pintail, 900 Shoveler and 4,200 Brent Geese have been recorded. The concentrations of all except the Mallard are of international importance. Castlemaine is not quite so important for waders, but 2,350 Oystercatchers, 4,000 Curlew, 3,000 Bar-tailed Godwits, 300 Redshanks, 3,000 Knot and 2,200 Dunlin have been recorded as well as several thousand Lapwing and up to 3,000 Golden Plover. Several hundred Common Scoters occur outside the estuary. Part of the area is now the subject of an annual no-shooting Order.

Lough Gill

Lough Gill is a shallow lake with rough pasture on its inland side and sand dunes protecting it from the sea. Reed beds of varying extent fringe the entire lake. An outlet to the sea is controlled by a sluice gate.

The lake is very productive and supports large numbers of ducks and swans, including both Whooper (up to 110) and Bewick's Swans (up to 98). Up to 600 Mallard, 4,000 Teal, 200 Gadwall, 500 Wigeon, 1,500 Shoveler, 2,000 Tufted Duck, 600 Pochard and 2,000 Coots have been counted, but there have been very few thorough counts in recent years. The count of Gadwall above was quite exceptional; normally 50-100 are present in winter, but these numbers alone are of national importance.

The vicinity of Lough Gill is at the centre of the Irish distribution of the Natterjack Toad, Ireland's only species of toad.

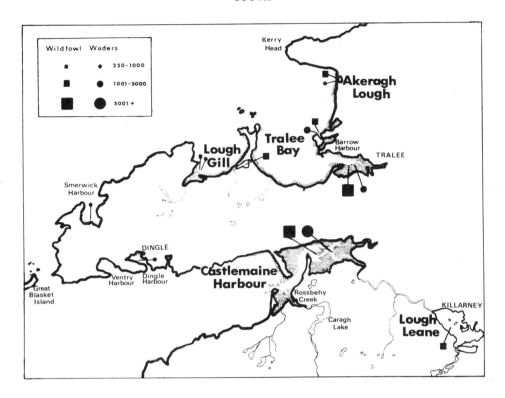

Fig. 10. Principal concentrations of wildfowl and waders in west Kerry

Tralee Bay and Barrow Harbour

The Tralee Bay and Barrow Harbour complex lies on the north side of the Dingle peninsula and is complementary to Castlemaine Harbour on the south side. There are extensive mudflats at the eastern end of Tralee Bay and in Barrow Harbour, which has developed behind a sand bar. Tralee Bay has a substantial area of salt marsh. *Zostera* grows quite widely in the area.

Like Castlemaine Harbour this is a very difficult area to count and most of the available data is based on aerial surveys. Up to 300 Mallard, 1,800 Teal, 4,500 Wigeon, 500 Pintail, 200 Shoveler and 3,200 Brent Geese have been counted, all of which, except Wigeon, represent numbers of international importance. However, there may be interchange between Tralee Bay and Castlemaine and the largest counts at Tralee Bay may have included many birds disturbed from Castlemaine. Outside the estuary there is a flock of several hundred Common Scoters.

The wader population is considerably smaller than at Castlemaine Harbour. Over 1,000 Lapwing are regular, but numbers of shore waders are quite low. Several hundred Oystercatchers, Curlew, Redshanks and Dunlin are the most numerous.

Akeragh Lough

Akeragh Lough is a brackish lagoon behind a line of high sand dunes (Fig. 10) north of Tralee. In the summer it consists of three ponds connected by dykes; in winter the surrounding wet meadows flood and the area becomes a large, shallow lake.

Depending on the water level very large numbers of Teal (up to 3,500 have been counted) and small numbers of other duck species, including Gadwall, use the area. Large numbers of Lapwing (up to 10,000) and Curlew (up to 4,000) sometimes occur. The lough is internationally famous for the number of rare waders from North America which have been seen, mainly in autumn.

Sewage flows into the northern end of the lake and there is a continual danger of drainage.

Lough Leane

Lough Leane is the larger of the Killarney lakes (Fig. 10). It is located in spectacularly beautiful surroundings with heavily wooded precipitous slopes on the southern side. The bed of the lake is limestone.

The wildfowl have not been assessed since 1970-71 when two counts were made. The maximum counts included 200 Mallard, 700 Teal, 2,000 Tufted Duck, 900 Pochard and 1,000 Coots.

Lough Gur

Lough Gur is a shallow lake in Limerick, north of Kilmallock, which is best known for its archaeological remains centred on a crannog.

Maximum counts of 1,600 wildfowl were recorded in 1971-72, 1,800 in 1972-73 and 1,300 in 1974-75. There were no counts in 1973-74. Maxima of 81 Mallard, 159 Teal, 700 Wigeon, 260 Shoveler and 450 Tufted Duck were included.

The lake is the subject of an annual no-shooting Order.

RIVER SHANNON

The Shannon is the longest river in Ireland. If considered as a unit with its tributaries and estuary it is much the most important wetland in the country, supporting enormous winter populations of ducks, swans and waders on the callows, or water-meadows, along its banks and those of its tributaries in the central lowlands, on its large lakes and on the mudflats and salt marshes of the estuary.

The river rises as an underground stream at the Shannon Pot on the Leitrim plateau, 150 metres above sea-level. It drops 100 metres over 14 kilometres before entering Lough Allen, but from the northern end of this lake to the southern end of Lough Derg, 300 kilometres away, the river drops only a further 30 metres. In the course of this long, slow meander across the lowlands the Shannon forms two great lakes, Lough Ree and Lough Derg, and collects a number of tributaries. South of Lough Derg the river once descended through spectacular rapids to the estuary at Limerick. Nowadays it is led through a canal to the electricity generating station at Ardnacrusha and the natural river course carries much less water than before the powerstation was built in the late 1920s. At Limerick tidal waters are met and the river broadens out into a great estuary with extensive mudflats, especially in the area where the estuary of the Fergus river meets the Shannon. The river is 345 kilometres from source to estuary and the estuary stretches for a further 80 kilometres.

Every winter the river and its tributaries overflow their banks, creating large expanses of floodwater on rich alluvial soil which provide feeding for surface-feeding ducks, Pochard, Tufted Duck, geese, swans and waders. Drainage of the areas where flooding is most frequent, particularly the section of the Shannon between Lough Ree and Lough Derg and the Little Brosna, has frequently been suggested. Such a step would decrease the area of callows available for birds and clearly would reduce their numbers. However, large-scale drainage is unlikely as the cost would be enormous and the benefit questionable. Once the callows have dried out in the summer they provide better pasture for feeding cattle than most of the surrounding agricultural land. A scheme whereby standing water could be drained off the callows at the end of March would be an appropriate compromise between the needs of agriculture and the requirements of the waterfowl. Water frequently remains to the end of April, but the great majority of the birds have left by the end of March.

Deposition of waste peat from Bord na Mona's turf cutting operations is another problem as it appears to add to the extent of the flooding on the Little Brosna. These operations, which are rapidly cleaning out the raised bogs of Ireland, may well have a further impact on the birds by removing refuges from shooting-pressure for the declining White-fronted Goose population of the Shannon valley.

Industrial development is the main threat to the Shannon estuary. In itself industrial development, if properly planned, need not affect the waterfowl population. At present the industrial estate at Shannon Airport, the oil-fired generating station at Tarbert and some industry at Foynes have no apparent effect on the birds. Future plans must ensure that the Fergus estuary and the shoreline from Aughinish Island east to

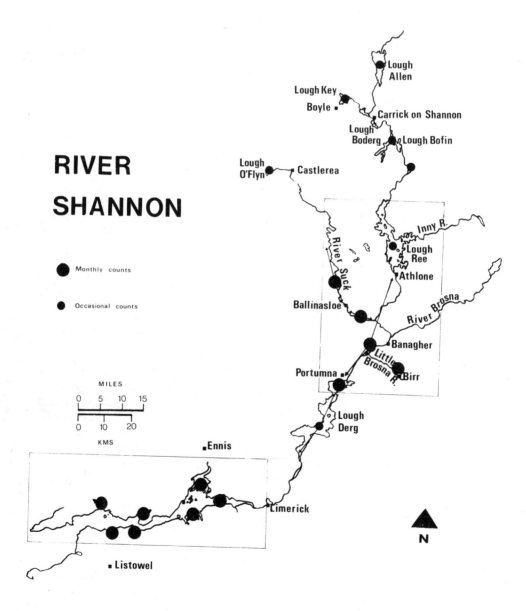

Fig. 11. Extent of coverage on the River Shannon and its estuary

Limerick are secure. This means that these areas must be kept free from pollution, especially oil pollution, and that new industries should be sited downstream of the narrow neck of the estuary between Foynes and Killadysert as heretofore. A secondary threat is posed by the spread of *Spartina* at the head of most of the inlets on the estuary, but this is not yet a serious problem.

The birds of the River Shannon, its tributaries and estuary were very little known until this survey commenced. Aside from an assessment of the goose numbers over 20 years ago (Ruttledge and Hall Watt 1958) and the inclusion of the area in an aerial survey of the wildfowl of Ireland (Cabot 1967b) no systematic observations were published prior to 1971 when this survey began. The river is very difficult to cover, because roads tend to run at right-angles to the bank, rather than parallel to it. The estuary is equally difficult because of its great length and breadth. Ground counts have been made occasionally of most sections of the river and estuary, and frequently of the Little Brosna, but the bulk of the data on which this account rests is derived from monthly aerial censuses of the rivers Suck and Little Brosna since 1972-73 and of the Shannon between Athlone and Portumna and the Shannon estuary since 1973-74. Without these systematic counts we would still know relatively little of the real importance of these areas.

The most numerous duck species on the Shannon is the Wigeon. On the river, its tributaries and the estuary there is a winter population of up to 25,000 birds. Teal numbers are much lower, but may total as many as 8,000. The river is extremely important for wild swans, both Whooper and Bewick's, and the total population is probably well over 1,000 with Whooper Swans in the great majority. There are small parties of White-fronted Geese at a number of locations and a total of 600-1,000 may be involved. On any visit to the Shannon valley the most obvious waders are Lapwing and Golden Plover. Nobody has ever counted them satisfactorily on long stretches of the river: they are easily missed in fields some distance from the flight path of an aircraft. But the winter population of each certainly exceeds 50,000 birds. Dunlin are the next most common wader. Close to 30,000 winter on the Shannon estuary and small parties of a few hundred on the callows. In spring the callows and the estuary are extremely important for Black-tailed Godwits as they pass through on their return journey to Iceland. Relatively small numbers winter, but up to 4,000 have been recorded on the Little Brosna, 1,000 on the Shannon between Shannonbridge and Athlone and 16,400 on the estuary. In summer the reed beds which fringe so much of the river provide nesting habitat for Mallard, Teal, Mute Swans and Coots as well as Great Crested Grebes, Little Grebes, Tufted Duck and Moorhens on the lakes or where the river is exceptionally broad.

Since this particular regional division is one gigantic wetland, rather than a division of land containing a scattering of wetlands, it is treated as such in the pages which follow. Commencing at Lough Allen in the north the birds of the river and its tributaries are considered in detail on a section by section basis.

Lough Allen

Although extensive in area (Fig. 11) Lough Allen holds very few waterfowl. A count of the entire lake in February 1975 produced totals of only 78 ducks, 32 swans and a few Lapwing and Curlew. (Cabot 1967b) in his aerial survey appears to have found nothing more than a few swans.

Lough Allen to Lough Ree

Immediately south of Lough Allen the Shannon meanders through drumlins for about half its journey to Lough Ree. So far as we know the stretch of river between Lough Allen and Carrick-on-Shannon is relatively unimportant for wildfowl, though Cabot counted 272 wild swans from the air in this section and Drumharlow Lough in January 1967. From Lough Key in the west the Boyle river flows through Oakport and Drumharlow Loughs to join the Shannon just north of Carrick-on-Shannon (Fig. 11). Lough Key holds small numbers (less than 50 each) of Teal, Tufted Duck, Pochard and Mute Swans, and slightly larger numbers of Mallard, Wigeon and wild swans. On a cruise through Oakport and Drumharlow Loughs in November 1973 small numbers (less than 60 each) of Mallard, Teal, Tufted Duck, Pochard, Mute and Whooper Swans were seen. However, there are extensive reed beds and some birds may have been missed.

South of Carrick-on-Shannon the River Shannon meanders through a series of small reed-fringed lakes and into the larger twin lakes of Boderg and Bofin (Fig. 11). Lough Boderg is fed from the south-west by two further lakes, Kilglass and Grange Loughs. In November 1973 nearly 300 Mallard, 120 Teal and smaller numbers of Wigeon, Tufted Duck, Goldeneye, White-fronted Geese, Mute and Whooper Swans were counted from a boat cruising over most of this complex of lakes, but excluding Lough Bofin. Cabot found 84 wild swans in 1967 but no ducks. Although the callows on this stretch of the river are completely water-logged and overgrown with reeds there are small flocks of Lapwing, Golden Plover and Curlew at intervals along the edge of the river.

The river emerges south of Lough Bofin from the more tortuous meanders of the drumlin country and flows via Lough Forbes reasonably directly to Lough Ree. This stretch of the river appears to hae very low numbers of wildfowl, though Cabot counted 390 wild swans from the air in January 1967 on the river between Lough Bofin and Lough Ree and found 26 White-fronted Geese at Lough Forbes, and there is now a concentration of approximately 400 White-fronted Geese at Lough Forbes.

Lough Ree

Lough Ree (Fig. 12) is the fifth largest lake in Ireland being, at some 10,500 hectares in area, slightly smaller than Lough Derg, its companion lake to the south. Most of the lake is quite shallow, less than ten metres in depth. The shoreline is long and highly indented. The edge is mostly stony and there are few reed beds, even in the bays.

Our information on the birds of the lake is based largely on a ground count of the entire area carried out at the beginning of February 1975 and another ground count of the east side at the end of the same month. At the time of the earlier count the water-level was exceptionally high, there was considerable flooding and some of the minor roads were inaccessible. When the second count was made the water had gone down to its normal level and the number of birds had increased enormously. The most important ornithological feature of the lake is its concentration of Tufted Duck. On the first count, with the level high, only 300 were counted on the north-east side of the lake; on the second count 1,200 were counted in the same section. A similar increase

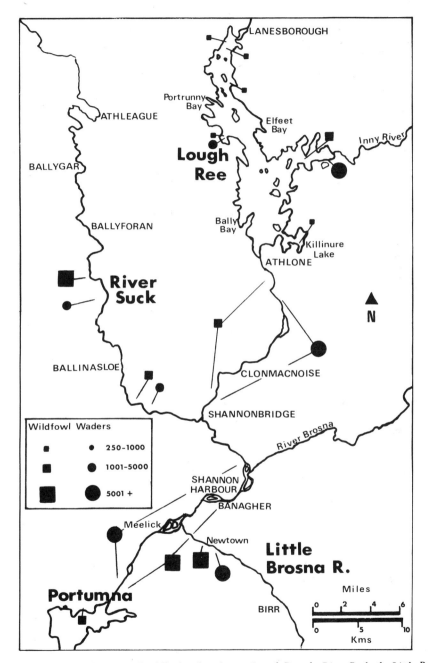

Fig. 12. Principal concentrations of wildfowl and waders on Lough Ree, the River Suck, the Little Brosna and the Shannon river between Lough Ree and Lough Derg.

was recorded in Wigeon numbers. The figures summarised at Tables 17, 18 and 19 are based on those of the second count of the north-east added to the figures obtained from the earlier count for the remainder of the lake. Because of the fluctuations in numbers these are obviously only a guide and further work is urgently needed to assess more precisely the importance of this lake.

River Shannon between Lough Ree and Lough Derg

From Lough Ree south to Lough Derg the Shannon is surrounded by extensive bogs and poorly drained agricultural land as it traverses the central lowlands. The only river crossings are at Athlone, Shannonbridge and Banagher where eskers, which formed under the glacial ice-sheet, provide firm ground on either bank. The flood plain of the river is pasture flooded in winter and known as callow land. These callows stretch along the bank of much of this section of the river.

The most numerous wildfowl are Wigeon and several thousand occur along the river between Athlone and Portumna (Table 17). Slightly more occur south of Shannonbridge than between Shannonbridge and Athlone. Several hundred Teal and wild swans, together with a small number of White-fronted Geese (Table 17), also winter along the river. However, there is considerable movement of birds in this area in response to changes in water level and shooting pressure. As a result certain areas may have no ducks at all on some occasions, but several hundred at other times. This movement also includes the birds on the River Suck and, especially, the Little Brosna river. The most exciting feature of this section of the Shannon is the sheer wildness of

Table 17

Average numbers of the most common species recorded in the peak month at selected sections of the Shannon valley, 1971-72 to 1974-75. Conventions are as in Table 5.

| | Lough Ree | River Shannon | | River Suck | | Little Brosna | Portumna |
		Athlone to Banagher	Banagher to Portumna	Ballyforan to Ballina-loe	Ballina-sloe to Shannon-bridge		
Mallard	100	600	100	—	—	100	1,200
Teal	600	600	1,000	600	300	800	900
Wigeon	1,100	3,200	4,500	2,800	2,600	7,300**	1,200
Pintail	—	—	—	—	—	100	—
Shoveler	—	—	100	—	—	200	—
Tufted Duck	1,700	—	—	—	—	—	—
Pochard	200	—	—	—	—	—	—
White-f Goose	—	100	200**	100	—	300**	—
Mute Swan	—	100	200	—	—	100	100
Whooper Swan	⎤	300**	⎤ 400**	100*	100*	100	—
Bewick's Swan	⎦		⎦	100**	200**	100**	—
Lapwing	4,600	2,200	5,300	3,500	1,100	6,100	—
G. Plover	1,800	2,400	5,500	3,600	—	5,600	—
Curlew	400	600	1,200	—	—	300	—
Black-t Godwit	—	500**	500**	—	—	2,500**	—

the place, a wildness which is accentuated by the relative difficulty of access from the ground. This gives the birds some security from the shooting pressure which is very intensive at weekends, though wildfowling from boats with engines is a problem in some parts.

Lapwing and Golden Plover congregate on the callows and fields behind the callows in very large numbers. Many more are present than the aerial counts disclose (Table 17), for the aircraft follows the line of the river. Counting of Golden Plover is difficult also because the birds rise and disappear before the observer in an aircraft can see them.

Table 18

Maximum numbers of ducks, geese and swans counted at selected sections of the Shannon system, 1971-72 to 1974-75 (NC indicates no count. An asterisk indicates that no count was carried out in December, January or February).

	1971-72	1972-73	1973-74	1974-75
Little Brosna	6,200	7,400	14,800	16,300
Suck (upper)	NC	⎤	3,600	7,100*
Suck (lower)	NC	⎥ 3,600	3,600	700*
Shannon (Shannonbridge to Portumna)	NC	NC	5,800	1,900*
Shannon (Athlone to Shannonbridge)	NC	NC	4,600	2,000*
Portumna	NC	NC	3,800	5,400
Lough Ree	NC	NC	NC	3,900

River Suck

The Suck is a long, narrow river rising just north of Lough O'Flyn in Roscommon (Fig. 11) and flowing in a south-south-easterly direction to join the Shannon near Shannonbridge (Fig. 12). Surrounding land use is very similar to that along the central part of the river Shannon. The land is poorly drained and there are large bogs close to the river. The callows at Muckanagh just north of Ballyforan are among the most important sections of the river. There are also callows between Ballyforan and the town of Ballinasloe and between Ballinasloe and the junction with the Shannon at Shannonbridge.

Lough O'Flyn, near the head of the river, holds up to 150 Tufted Duck and 50-250 Pochard, though 650 were counted on one occasion. Small numbers of dabbling ducks and swans also occur in winter. The waterfowl population between Lough O'Flyn and Ballygar (Fig. 12) has only occasionally been counted, but up to 800 Wigeon and 60 Whooper Swans are known to have occurred. At Muckanagh, between Ballygar and Ballyforan, there are callows of importance for a small White-fronted Goose population.

From Ballyforan to the junction with the Shannon there are large flocks of Wigeon every winter. Numbers fluctuate, but up to 5,400 have been counted on the river. Both Whooper and Bewick's Swans occur along the river in numbers of international importance (Table 17). The callows have huge numbers of Lapwing and Golden Plover. In 1972-73 some 16,000 waders were counted between Ballyforan and Shannonbridge, the great majority of which were Lapwing. Like so much of the Shannon system this area needs further study to adequately assess its importance.

Table 19

Maximum numbers of waders counted at selected sections of the Shannon system, 1971-72 to 1974-75 (NC indicates no count). An asterisk indicates that no count was carried out in December, January or February).

	1971-72	1972-73	1973-74	1974-75
Little Brosna	15,600	19,200	18,600	23,000
Suck (upper)	NC	16,000	7,100	1,700*
Suck (lower)	NC		1,200	1,100*
Shannon (Shannonbridge to Portumna)	NC	NC	9,600	10,300
Shannon (Athlone to Shannonbridge)	NC	NC	5,300	1,700*
Lough Ree	NC	NC	NC	8,800*

Little Brosna river and flooded cellows

Little Brosna River

The important part of the Little Brosna for waterfowl comprises the callows on both sides of the river, extending from New Bridge, seven kilometres north-west of Birr (Fig. 12), to the junction with the Shannon at Meelick and includes Big Island and Friar's Island on the Shannon.

As a wildfowl haunt it is extremely important. The maximum figure for wildfowl recorded in winter 1974-75, for example, exceeded the number recorded at Wexford Harbour and Slobs in any of the four years covered by this survey. The most numerous species is the Wigeon, of which the Little Brosna holds an internationally important population. In mid-winter up to 7,000 are present, but many more concentrate in the area in spring. The highest count so far recorded is of 13,800 in March 1975. Large numbers of Teal (up to 2,200) and the biggest flock of Pintail on the Shannon system also occur. The callows are the feeding ground for several hundred White-fronted Geese, the second largest concentration in Ireland after the Wexford slobs. Some of the largest numbers of Lapwing and Golden Plover in Ireland scatter over the callows and adjoining farmland, but the most important wader concentration is the flock of Black-tailed Godwits which peaks in late winter at up to 4,000 birds. Even in January when closer to 1,000 are present this is the biggest inland flock in Ireland. Dunlin are also recorded in winter and up to 1,390 have been counted.

Drainage of the area has been suggested but the establishment of part of it as a no-shooting area by ministerial Order indicates some commitment to conserve the Little Brosna's birds. It is one of the most magnificent places in Ireland to watch great flocks of wildfowl. One can only hope that conservation measures will extend to conserving the habitat as well as prohibiting shooting over a section.

Portumna

In the north-west corner of Lough Derg a state owned section of the shoreline has been developed as a wildfowl sanctuary. A number of islands provide nesting sites for Mallard and Tufted Duck. Opposite the islands a 20 hectare area is flooded annually in winter by means of an embankment to provide feeding for dabbling ducks. The measure has obviously been successful for the area has a large population of Mallard. Teal and Wigeon (Table 17). Although admittedly artificially maintained the Mallard numbers are among the highest in Ireland.

Lough Derg to Limerick

Little is known in detail of the waterfowl occurring between Lough Derg and the head of the estuary at Limerick. From the aerial census it would appear that very few wildfowl winter in the area, apart from small White-fronted Goose flocks in the north-east corner of Lough Derg, some 70-100 Mute Swans and small scattered flocks of diving duck on the lough. Below Killaloe there are few waterfowl until one reaches the stretch of river just above Limerick city where parties of wild and Mute Swans occur when there are floods.

Shannon Estuary

The Shannon estuary is the largest estuarine complex in Ireland. It stretches for approximately 80 kilometres and varies from less than one to over 15 kilometres in width. The estuary is a drowned river valley, edged with sand and mud banks, and with many square kilometres of inter-tidal mudflat in the inlets on both sides of the estuary. All the small rivers flowing into the estuary deposit large quantities of silt in times of flood. In some parts, particularly on the Fergus estuary, land has been reclaimed and is protected by embankments. On the west side of the upper Fergus estuary at Islandavanna *Spartina* has been planted to accelerate the process of reclamation.

The estuary is internationally important for wildfowl and waders, holding well over 10,000 wildfowl (Table 20) and 20,000 waders (Table 21). Taking each species individually, it has internationally important populations of Teal, Wigeon, Shoveler, Black-tailed Godwits, Bar-tailed Godwits, Redshank and Dunlin and nationally important populations of Scaup, Shelduck, Greylag Geese and Whooper Swans. The Wigeon and Dunlin numbers represent 2% of the estimated north-west European winter populations, but the Black-tailed Godwit peak can be as high as 50% of the total estimated Icelandic breeding population. Numbers in late March and early April are always high, and 16,400 in April 1974 was much the largest concentration ever recorded in Ireland and Britain combined.

In winter numbers are generally lower. The most numerous species by far is the Dunlin. These birds reach a peak about January when over 30,000 have been counted. The great majority feed in the Fergus estuary.

As a guide to assessing the significance of each section of the estuary maximum wildfowl and wader numbers for each main division, together with totals for the entire estuary, are set out at Tables 20 and 21. From these tables the importance of the Fergus estuary and the mudflats around Shannon Airport, Aughinish Island and the upper estuary generally is very clear. Poulnasherry Bay and Clonderalaw Bay are the most important bays below the neck of the estuary at Foynes.

Table 20

Maximum numbers of ducks, geese and swans counted in sections of the Shannon estuary and in the total estuary, 1972-73 to 1974-75. There was only one total count in 1972-73.

	1972-73	1973-74	1974-75
Total estuary	10,200	15,400	14,300
Fergus estuary	2,100	6,200	4,000
Shannon Airport area	3,400	4,100	2,600
Aughinish Island area	1,300	3,700	3,600
Beagh Castle to Limerick	700	3,600	800
Poulnasherry Bay	1,600	1,600	2,800
Tarbert	1,100	1,100	2,000
Clonderalaw Bay	1,100	1,700	1,500
Ballylongford Bay	500	1,000	200

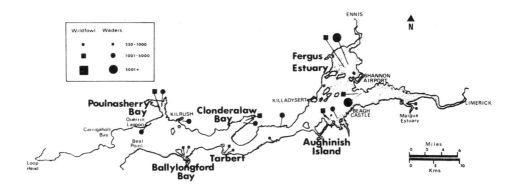

Fig. 13. Principal concentration of wildfowl and waders on the Shannon estuary

The great threat to the birds of the estuary is industrial development. This magnificent expanse of estuary has already been scarred by the construction of an oil-fired generating station at Tarbert. The birds, however, can live with unattractive buildings. What they cannot tolerate is certain forms of pollution and reclamation of the estuary. Planning for future developments must take into account the potential risk to the tens of thousands of wildfowl and waders which feed on the mudflats of the upper estuary. One oil spillage on a rising tide could cause enormous mortality.

Although the state owns a large section of the west side of the Fergus estuary no management practices have yet been introduced. Portion of the estuary could readily be developed into an attractive reserve for the public to view birds.

Table 21

Maximum numbers of waders recorded in sections of the Shannon estuary and in the total estuary, 1972-73 to 1974-75. There was only one total count in 1972-73.

	1972-73	1973-74	1974-75
Total estuary	48,800	67,600	38,200
Fergus estuary	34,300	39,300	21,400
Shannon Airport area	7,100	31,600	21,300
Beagh Castle to Limerick	2,700	7,100	1,000
Aughinish Island area	1,800	4,200	4,600
Poulnasherry Bay	2,400	3,400	1,300
Ballylongford Bay	900	3,800	2,200
Clonderalaw Bay	3,200	2,400	1,100
Tarbert	1,700	2,500	2,100

Table 22

Average numbers of the most common species recorded in the peak month at selected sections of the Shannon estuary and in the total estuary, 1972-73 to 1974-75. Conventions are as in Table 5.

	Total estuary	Fergus estuary	Shannon Airport area	Aughinish Island area	Beagh Castle to Limerick	Poulna-sherry Bay
Mallard	600	100	300	300	—	100
Teal	2,500**	900	1,200	1,500**	400	500
Wigeon	9,900**	4,300**	1,700	2,600	700	1,100
Shoveler	200**	200**	100	—	—	—
Scaup	200*	200*	100*	100*	—	200*
Shelduck	1,000*	200	100	200	100	200
Greylag Goose	100*	—	—	—	—	—
Brent Goose	300	—	—	—	—	300
Mute Swan	100	—	—	—	—	—
Whooper Swan	100*	—	—	—	—	—
Coot	200	—	200	—	—	—
Oystercatcher	400	—	100	100	—	—
Lapwing	4,900	1,400	4,200	700	500	1,600
Grey Plover	200	200	—	—	—	—
Golden Plover	2,600	2,600	2,000	300	200	400
Curlew	3,200**	500	200	1,900**	100	700
Black-t. Godwit	8,400**	6,600**	4,900**	300	800	—
Bar-t. Godwit	1,200**	200	1,200**	—	—	—
Redshank	3,200**	1,700**	800	600	200	200
Greenshank	100	—	—	—	—	—
Knot	2,500	800	2,500	—	300	100
Dunlin	29,600**	14,800**	7,000	1,500	1,900	800

WEST

In this chapter the west is defined as that part of the country which lies north of the Shannon estuary and west of the river Shannon, but excludes most of Sligo, north Roscommon and a small section of east Mayo (Fig. 14). It includes all of Clare and Galway and almost all of Roscommon and Mayo.

The coast of the west of Ireland is long and frequently broken with small inlets, but very few have sufficient inter-tidal mud to support even small populations of waders. Only Liscannor Bay, Galway Bay, Clew Bay, Blacksod Bay, Broadhaven Bay and Killala Bay hold moderate concentrations of waders. However, there are long stretches of sandy beach on the west Galway and Mayo coast which hold considerable numbers of Ringed Plover and Sanderling, but as these beaches are long and hold few other birds there have been very few counts by ornithologists.

Inland the terrain is very varied, though much of the land is poor for agriculture and the farms are generally small. Clare is best known as a limestone county, with the most famous limestone landscape in Ireland — the Burren — in the north-west. On the south-eastern fringe of this strange area of pale grey hills lies a series of lakes including both turloughs and permanent bodies of water. From Ballyallia Lake, near Ennis, in the south-west to Coole Lake, near Gort, in the north-east the lakes follow the grain of the land. Many of them hold large numbers of ducks which move about between the lakes and the Shannon estuary, but geese and shore waders are quite scarce. South-west Clare is quite different, a landscape of windswept sandstone and shale with very few lakes or lagoons.

North and north-east of Clare limestone plains are the predominant feature of the landscape. Only the Slieve Aughty mountains on the west side of Lough Derg relieve the flatness significantly. The land of east Galway and Roscommon is not bare like the Burren, but the covering of glacial drift is thin over most of the area. Bogs are widespread around the Suck and the Shannon and often cover several square kilometres. Farms are generally small and agriculture is based on pasturage. The limestone in the area is pitted with sinkholes. Few rivers keep a permanent course and the most important wetlands for birds are turloughs.

Turloughs are lakes which in time of low rainfall become small lakes or ponds, or in some cases even dry out completely. After heavy rain, however, they fill up very quickly as the water table rises. Water emerges from underground springs through fissures in the bed of the turloughs. In summer turloughs are grazed by cattle and sheep. Their appearance is very distinctive when the water level is low, as the black moss *Cinclidotus fontinalus* covers the rocks and boulders below the level of the flood zone. Turloughs are widely scattered across east Connacht and provide excellent Wigeon habitat. The shallow floodwaters provide a relatively secure position from which the ducks can graze. They are not marked on maps and there are doubtless some very important turloughs for wildfowl which are still unknown to ornithologists. The best known turlough, and almost certainly the most important for birds, is that at Rahasane near Craughwell in Galway. In Roscommon the turloughs are also widely

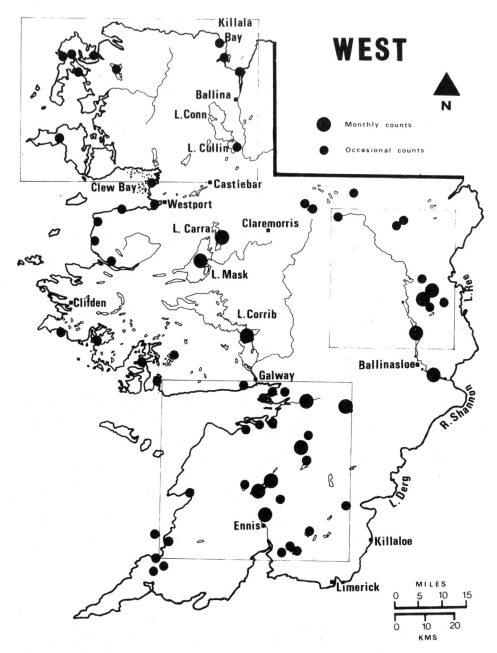

Fig. 14. Extent of coverage at wetlands in the West

used by Wigeon and other ducks, but the birds alternate between these sites and the river Suck, dealt with in the chapter on the Shannon.

West Galway and Mayo are very different from the east, though the large Galway and Mayo lakes have been attributed to some extent to the same vulnerability of limestone to chemical weathering or solution which has helped create turloughs, though the great depth of these lakes indicates that glacial scour has also played a part in their evolution (Freeman 1969). The landscape of west Connacht is impressively beautiful with great mountains, broad valleys, large and small lakes, long, narrow sea inlets and a large number of islands. South of Clew Bay are ancient sedimentary rocks and granite. To the north are sandstones, schists and quartzites with limestone extending to the coast at Clew Bay. Much of the area is mountainous. In south Galway and west Mayo there are huge expanses of blanket bog. Around Westport drumlins cover the lowland and form an archipelago in Clew Bay. The majority of the lakes which abound in west Galway are acidic and only a few are of importance for birds.

The main threat to the wetlands of the west of Ireland is drainage. Many of the turloughs have already been drained and some of those which remain are threatened. In particular, there have been plans prepared for the drainage of Rahasane, the last remaining turlough of any size in the country.

The birds of the west of Ireland are less well-known than those of Ireland east and south of the Shannon. An old paper on the birds of Galway and Mayo (Ruttledge 1950) and, more recently, booklets on the birds of Clare and Limerick (Stapleton 1975) and Galway and Mayo (Whilde 1977) are the main works on the birds of the area.

Because of the great extent of this part of Ireland and the relatively small amount of quantitative data on the waterfowl of the area it is difficult to comment on individual species. It is unquestionable, however, that the most abundant duck is the Wigeon. The total in the area is difficult to estimate because of the amount of suitable habitat available but at its peak is somewhere between 20,000 and 24,000 each year. In autumn Pochard are extremely numerous, but are concentrated at Lough Corrib where 12,000-15,000 and in some years over 20,000 assemble in a great raft. After November they disperse rapidly, very much smaller numbers remaining in the west of Ireland by Christmas. Coots are also very abundant, up to 16,000 having been counted at Lough Corrib and 2,350 at Lough Rea. White-fronted Geese and Whooper and Bewick's Swans are widespread in quite small numbers. The area does not hold great numbers of any species of shore wader but Lapwing and Golden Plover are widespread and numerous in winter. Curlew are common inland and on the coast.

The area is very important for nesting wildfowl and waders. One of the biggest concentrations of nesting Mallard in the country is at Lough Carra. Teal, Tufted Duck and Red-breasted Mergansers nest thinly but widely. Pintail, Shoveler and Pochard are scarce nesting species. Common Scoter nest at Lough Conn and have been recorded at Lough Carra. Shelduck nest along the coastline. Among the waders Lapwing, Snipe, Curlew and Common Sandpipers are widespread and common breeding birds. Oystercatchers and Ringed Plover are also common but the former is restricted to the coast and the latter to the coast and larger lakes. Redshanks nest in the eastern part of the area. Golden Plover are restricted to the mountainous parts of Galway and Mayo. Woodcocks appear to be fairly widely distributed. Dunlin nest on callows and

moorland but, while widely scattered, are very scarce. However, this is the centre of
the Irish breeding population.

It is essential to emphasise yet again that the birds of the west and north-west are the
least known birds in Ireland. Regular counts of the waterfowl have only been made at
those wetlands believed to be of the greatest importance. Only occasional counts have
been made at many others which, if they had been situated on the east or south coasts,
would have been counted every month and probably considered as of some
importance. The reader should bear this in mind in considering the accounts which
follow of individual wetlands. We have a great deal of data, but our conclusions on
many sites must still be only tentative. The wetland accounts commence with the Clare
wetlands and then those of Galway, Roscommon and Mayo in that order. The river
Suck, which flows through Roscommon and Galway, has been dealt with in the
chapter on the Shannon.

The most important Clare wetlands are the lakes, and the most significant of these
are described first, in the approximate order of their importance. Then the coastal
wetlands are described, working north-east along the coast from Loop Head. The
estuaries opening onto the mouth of the Shannon have already been discussed in the
chapter on the Shannon.

Ballyallia Lake

Ballyallia Lake is a small lake of 35 hectares on the River Fergus north of Ennis (Fig. 15). The lake is very shallow, but the waterbody is permanent, though it is situated in a limestone depression. The edge of the lake is used for cattle grazing. There is a public car-park at the eastern end.

Ballyallia is one of Ireland's great wildfowl lakes. The concentration of up to 5,000 ducks on such a small lake presents a remarkable sight. The populations of up to 100 Gadwall (180 in 1977-78) and 500 Shoveler are of international importance. The number of Wigeon fluctuates considerably, but as many as 3,300 have been counted. Mallard, Teal, Tufted Duck and Pochard are all relatively abundant (Table 23). Small numbers of Whooper and Bewick's Swans occur, mostly in the north-east corner of the lake, but it is exceptional to see more than 30 of either. Several hundred Coots winter also. Some waders occur. Lapwing are present in winter in numbers up to 500, and up to 700 Curlew and a similar number of Black-tailed Godwits frequent the shore. In summer Great Crested Grebes breed.

The lake is the subject of an annual no-shooting Order. It has been developed by Clare County Council as a recreation centre for the town of Ennis. The car-park is extensively used in summer when local people fish and swim in the lake. Since this use of the lake as an amenity is restricted to the summer there is no conflict with conservation interests.

Lough Atedaun

Lough Atedaun is a small, shallow lake just east of Corrofin which at times holds large numbers of ducks. Numbers fluctuate considerably, probably depending on the level of disturbance at this and other sites. The most numerous species is the Wigeon (Table 23). Large numbers of Teal and some Tufted Duck also occur, as well as small numbers of Pintail, Shoveler and Pochard.

This is a great swan lake. Up to 70 each of Mute, Whooper and Bewick's Swans occur each winter.

Ballyeighter Loughs

Ballyeighter Loughs stretch north-east from Loughs Atedaun and Cullaun (Fig. 15). They are also shallow and low-lying but have more extensive reedbeds and marshy land surrounding them.

These lakes hold populations of close to 200 Mallard and Teal and 1,500 Wigeon when at their best. A scattering of other species also occurs. Unfortunately, monthly counts were only carried out in one year and more information is urgently required.

Lough Cullaunyheeda

Lough Cullaunyheeda, situated about 20 kilometres east-south-east of Ennis, is a medium sized lake with a small population of up to 300 ducks. It has quite extensive reedbeds which hold Mallard and Teal and the open water is frequented by Tufted Duck, Pochard and up to 43 Goldeneye.

Tullaher Lough

Tullaher Lough is a small marshy lake in west Clare, situated almost directly between Poulnacherry Bay and Doonbeg. It holds small numbers of ducks (up to 250), most of which are Teal. Its chief significance is that it has a wintering population of about 50 White-fronted Geese.

Doonbeg Marsh

The marsh and river at Doonbeg in west Clare, situated just south of Mutton Island, flood in winter and attract up to 250 wildfowl. Barnacle Geese are occasional visitors.

Fig. 15. Principal concentrations of wildfowl and waders in Clare and north Galway

Table 23

Average numbers of the most common species recorded in the peak month at selected Clare and Galway lakes, 1971-72 to 1974-1975. Conventions are as in Table 5.

	Bally-allia Lake	Lough Atedaun	Bally-eighter Loughs	Coole Lake	Rahasane
Mallard	300	—	200	100	100
Teal	600	300	200	400	500
Gadwall	100	—	—	—	—
Wigeon	1,800	3,000	1,500	1,100	5,100**
Pintail	—	—	—	—	100
Shoveler	500**	—	—	—	300**
Tufted Duck	200	100	—	—	100
Pochard	100	—	—	200	100
White-fronted Goose	—	—	—	—	100**
Mute Swan	—	100	—	—	100
Whooper Swan	—	100*	—	—	100*
Bewick's Swan	—	100**	—	—	—
Coot	100	—	—	—	100
Lapwing	300	1,000	300	300	3,900
Golden Plover	—	500	—	1,300	3,200
Curlew	100	—	100	100	600
Black-tailed Godwit	100	—	—	—	—
Dunlin	—	100	—	—	100

Mutton Island

Mutton Island is a 75 hectare island lying just off the west coast of Clare. The island is windswept and rocky; the main vegetation is a rank maritime grass. The island had the second largest winter population of Barnacle Geese in Ireland during the period of these counts. From counts made at intervals since 1961 it appears that numbers can reach a maximum of 480 birds. Since 1976-77 it has been overtaken by Lissadell, Co. Sligo as a haunt.

Table 24

Maximum numbers of ducks, geese and swans counted at selected wetlands in Clare and south Galway, 1971-72 to 1974-75 (NC indicates no count).

	1971-72	1972-73	1973-74	1974-75
Rahasane	4,700	6,000	8,400	8,800
Ballyallia Lake	1,000	4,500	5,300	2,300
Lough Atedaun	900	1,000	3,500	300
Coole Lake	NC	2,400	2,300	1,100
Ballyeighter Loughs	NC	NC	2,100	500

Lurga Point

Lurga Point is directly opposite Mutton Island on the west coast. There are rocks and a rather sandy inter-tidal zone. In winter up to 750 waders occur. Most are Dunlin (up to 500), Sanderling (up to 100) ánd Purple Sandpipers (up to 70).

Spanish Point

The strand at Spanish Point, north of Quilty on the west coast of Clare, holds quite large numbers of Oystercatchers in winter (up to 100) and smaller numbers of Curlews and Redshanks.

Lahinch

The inter-tidal mudflats at Lahinch are one of the few places on the Clare coast which hold medium-sized flocks of both ducks and waders. Up to 250 Wigeon feed in the area and small numbers of Oystercatchers, Curlew and Redshanks, no more than 50 of each, occur. Out in the bay Common Scoters have been recorded.

Ballyvaughan Bay

The strip of coast from Ballyvaughan to New Quay on the south side of Galway Bay is a mixture of stony and sandy beaches with occasional small areas of inter-tidal mudflats. The area is well known as a haunt of 50-70 Brent Geese, but there has been only one wader count made. On that occasion 365 waders were counted, of which 150 were Curlew and 150 Dunlin.

The inland Galway wetlands are discussed next, in order from south to north, and then the most important coastal area — the Galway Bay complex — is considered.

Coole Lake

Coole Lake is a shallow lake on limestone, a few kilometres north-west of Gort. The lake is famous in literature for the swans of which W. B. Yeats wrote in his poem 'The wild swans at Coole', published in 1919 in the book of the same name, though his birds with 'the bell-beat of their wings' were clearly Mute Swans.

Wild swans do visit the lake, however, Whooper generally outnumbering Bewick's. Numbers vary, but 15-50 Whooper and up to 12 Bewick's occur each winter. The lake is also important for ducks, with up to 2,400 recorded (Table 24). The most numerous ducks are Wigeon and Teal, but Mallard, Tufted Duck and Pochard are usually present (Table 23). Pintail and Shoveler are scarcer but regular.

The lake is situated in the grounds of Coole Park, now owned by the state, and the lake is the subject of a no-shooting Order.

Lough Rea

Lough Rea is a medium sized lake of 260 hectares lying just south of Loughrea town. It is yet another of the limestone lakes which stretch north-west from south Clare. This lake is deeper than some of those already discussed and is a locally impor---t trout fishery.

O\ ⌐00 duck have been counted on the lake and about the same number of Coots. Up to 200 Wigeon, 600 Shoveler, 100 Tufted Duck and 200 Pochard have been recorded. Further data is required for this area; it is not known whether large numbers of ducks remain here for much of the winter or occur mainly when disturbed from other areas.

Rahasane

Rahasane is the largest remaining turlough in Ireland. It is located between Craughwell and Clarinbridge. In summer the area is green pasture with the narrow Dunkellin river flowing through it. Once the heavy winter rain comes and the water-table rises water bubbles up through swallow-holes. After heavy rain the river floods as well and a lake three kilometres long and almost a kilometre wide appears within hours. The floor of the turlough has a thick layer of fine alluvial silt. While the area is internationally important for its birds its significance transcends the purely ornithological. As one of the finest examples of a decreasing habitat unique to Ireland this wetland should be conserved as a matter of urgency.

The numbers of birds using the area fluctuate considerably, but up to 5,000 Wigeon are recorded each winter. Smaller numbers of Mallard, Teal, Pintail, Shoveler, Tufted Duck and Pochard also winter on the lake. A flock of up to 140 White-fronted Geese alternates between the lake and Rinville marsh, north-west of Clarinbridge. Flocks of varying numbers of Mute, Whooper and Bewick's Swans are almost always present in winter. Flocks of Lapwing and Golden Plover and small numbers of Black-tailed Godwits, Redshanks and Dunlin are also regular.

The blackthorn around the turlough is the habitat of one of Ireland's scarcest butterflies, the brown hairstreak. The fairy shrimp was first discovered in Ireland in this lake in 1975 (Young 1975).

The area is very heavily shot and there are plans for drainage.

Lough Corrib

Lough Corrib is the second largest lake in Ireland, with an area of 17,000 hectares. The lake can be divided into two main sections. The narrow south-eastern part is very shallow, with a maximum depth of about six metres, and lies on limestone. The much larger and wider northern part is considerably deeper and lies mainly on granite, schist, shales and sandstones. Depths of up to 45 metres have been recorded in the north-west corner (Flanagan and Toner 1975). Much of the lake is edged with bare limestone or with thin bog over the limestone. There is an extensive area of fen at the southern end of the lake which is a source of material for local thatchers. This is one of Ireland's great brown trout fishing lakes.

The most numerous species on the lake are Pochard and Coot. Pochard, mostly males, begin to build up on Lough Corrib from mid-July and reach a peak in October or November. Over 22,000 have been counted, representing almost 10% of the north-west European population. There is a rapid decline from November and only 2,000 or so remain into January and a few hundred into March. The pattern of occurrence of Coots is more complex, with peak numbers occurring in December in 1973-74 (7,000) and October in 1974-75 (11,600). Quite large numbers of Mallard, Teal and, particularly, Wigeon also occur in winter. Small numbers of Gadwall frequent the Mount Ross inlet. Tufted Duck are less numerous than Pochard but up to 800 occur.

Rahasane turlough, Co. Galway

Galway Bay

Galway Bay is a very broad bay with a series of narrow, shallow inlets at its eastern and southern sides. Because the inlets are complex in shape and access is difficult at many points there has never been a complete count of the wildfowl or waders of the entire bay from Ballyvaughan Bay east around to Galway town and Loc Ruisin. However, the area around Tawin Island has been counted on many occasions and all other sections of the bay have been visited on at least one occasion in winter for the purposes of this enquiry.

From the accumulated data, far from perfect though it is, it appears that Galway Bay holds quite large numbers of Teal (up to 150), Wigeon (up to 900), Red-breasted Mergansers (up to 120) and Brent Geese (up to 130). Smaller numbers of Mallard, Pintail, Shoveler and Shelduck also occur.

The most numerous shore waders are Oystercatchers (up to 300), Ringed Plover (up to 150), Turnstone (up to 250), Curlew (up to 400), Redshanks (up to 400) and Dunlin (up to 1,500). These numbers are minimal; almost certainly more birds frequent the creeks and narrow inlets which are difficult to count.

In Roscommon there are a number of lakes and turloughs which have been visited relatively irregularly but which are important for wildfowl. These are discussed in **alphabetical order.**

Castleplunket area

Several turloughs in the vicinity of Castleplunket — Brierfield, Castleplunket and Mullygollan — hold dabbling ducks and wild swans (Fig. 16). The most numerous ducks are Teal and Wigeon, at times 250 of each being recorded. Less numerous, but also regular, are Mallard, Pintail (up to 100), Shoveler, Tufted Duck and Pochard. The area holds very large numbers of both Whooper and Bewick's Swans. Counts of 122 Whooper and 213 Bewick's Swans have been recorded.

Cloonloughlin

Cloonloughlin (Fig. 16) is a turlough close to Mount Talbot where large numbers of ducks and waders occur. Since monthly counts began in 1973-74 maxima of 680 Teal, 1,300 Wigeon, 75 Pintail and 97 Shoveler have been recorded. Whooper and Bewick's Swans are occasional and usually occur only in very small parties.

The area holds up to 1,000 Lapwing, 2,000 Golden Plover and 500 Curlew in winter. A flock of up to 300 Dunlin is usually present as well. In spring Black-tailed Godwits (up to 800) and Redshanks (up to 50) occur around the edge.

Lough Croan

Lough Croan (Fig. 16) is a small, permanent lake which, like most of the surrounding lakes and the adjacent river Suck, supports quite large numbers of Teal (up to 250) and Wigeon (up to 900). As with these other areas smaller numbers of Mallard, Pintail and Shoveler also occur. The surrounding pasture supports flocks of Lapwing and Golden Plover.

G.D.R.

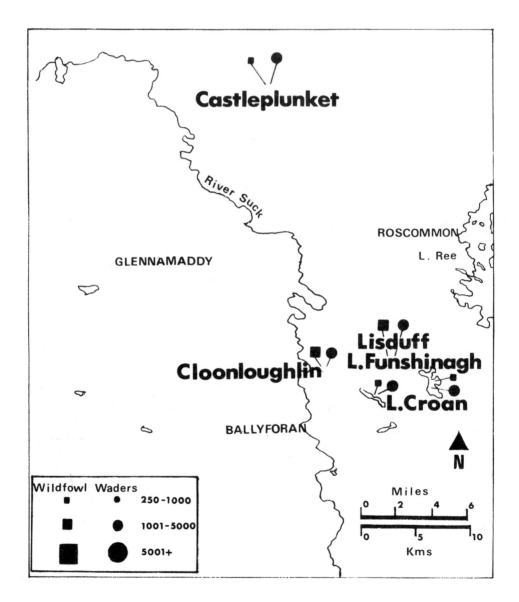

Fig. 16. Principal concentration of wildfowl and waders in the Roscommon area, excluding the River Suck

Lough Funshinagh

Once a famous wetland for breeding and wintering ducks Lough Funshinagh has become almost completely choked with *Phragmites* and ducks, if present, are extremely difficult to see. Small numbers of Mallard, Teal, Wigeon, Shoveler and, sometimes, diving ducks occur still in winter, but the area now holds many fewer birds than Lough Croan.

Lough Glinn

Lough Glinn is of some importance for diving ducks. It holds over 150 each of Tufted Duck and Pochard. Numbers of dabbling ducks and swans are much lower.

Lisduff

Lisduff turlough, also known as Keenagh, is one of the most important Roscommon wetlands, but the number of birds recorded there fluctuates enormously. Like Lough Croan and Cloonloughlin it is chiefly a Wigeon haunt, up to 1,200 having been counted. Much smaller numbers, rarely exceeding 100, of other species of ducks also occur. Around the verge Lapwing, Golden Plover, Curlew and Dunlin occur in small parties. A scattering of Redshanks are seen, mostly in spring, when Black-tailed Godwits (up to 380) also pass through.

Mayo has a number of large lakes, many turloughs and a scattering of smaller lakes which are of importance for wildfowl. Some, however, are much more important than others. These are discussed next, and they are followed by brief accounts of the more important coastal wetlands.

Lough Carra

Lough Carra is a 1,500 hectare lake forming part of the drainage systems of Loughs Corrib and Mask. It lies over limestone and is very shallow, the maximum depth being about nine metres (Flanagan and Toner 1975). There are extensive reed-beds around the edge of the lake and a number of wooded islands which were grazed by cattle until recently.

The lake is very important as a breeding area for Mallard and a wintering area for a number of species of ducks. The Mallard population is the subject of a long-term research project. In winter the lake holds up to 2,000 Mallard, though numbers usually fluctuate between 800 and 1,500. Peak numbers are normally recorded in autumn, but in some years there is a second peak in mid-winter. Ringing at the lake has shown, however, that the Mallard population is almost completely sedentary and that seasonal fluctuations are due to local movements. The lake also holds winter populations of up to 900 Teal, 50 Gadwall, 900 Wigeon, 500 Shoveler, 500 Tufted Duck, 850 Pochard and 75 Goldeneye. Numbers vary enormously, both from week to week and from year to year, and these figures are maxima. The Shoveler population is of international importance and the Mallard population of national importance.

Although the lake has been the subject of a no-shooting Order since 1969 and research on Mallard has been carried out since 1967 under state auspices there is a very real threat of drainage.

Lough Carrowmore

Lough Carrowmore is a medium-sized lake (960 hectares) in north-west Mayo and is surrounded by blanket bog (Fig. 17).

The lake is an important wintering area for diving ducks. Although only four counts of the lake have been recorded we know that it holds up to 240 Tufted Duck and 630 Pochard in winter. Very small numbers of dabbling ducks (less than 30 of any species) have also been recorded and up to 30 White-fronted Geese. The lake, however, is situated in the enormous Bog of Erris which holds a number of small parties of these geese.

Lough Conn

Lough Conn, though one of Ireland's larger lakes (5,000 hectares), is apparently not a very important wintering area for wildfowl. In summer, however, it holds a number of breeding pairs of Common Scoters. In 1968 a thorough survey showed a population of 28-31 pairs; a similar search in 1958 produced a total of 20-30 pairs.

The only detailed information on the birds of the lake in winter is a count of the west side in January 1969. This count showed small numbers of ducks to be present, the most numerous being Teal (61 birds), and a party of 38 White-fronted Geese.

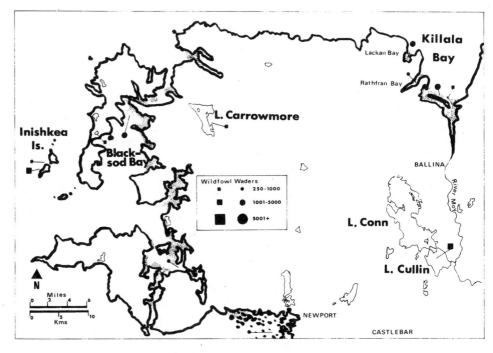

Fig. 17. Principal concentration of wildfowl and waders in Mayo

Lough Cullin

Lough Cullin is a medium-sized lake of 1,100 hectares at the southern end of Lough Conn (Fig. 17). Very little data is available on the birds of the area but it is known to be of great importance for diving ducks is autumn. A flock of at least 4,000 was present at the end of July 1975 and included both Tufted Duck and Pochard, but the proportion of each could not be ascertained. Counts in December and March in other years produced totals of 300 Tufted Duck and 220 Pochard in December, but only 100 Tufted Duck and no Pochard at all in March.

This lake demands a great deal more investigation.

Dooaghtry Lakes

Dooaghtry Lakes, south of Killadoon, on the south Mayo coast are probably the most important of a series of small lakes behind the beach which runs from Roonah Quay south almost to Killary Harbour. These lakes hold up to 200 Wigeon in winter and smaller numbers of Mallard, Teal and diving duck. Close to 40 each of Mute and Whooper Swans have been recorded.

Lough Mask

Since Lough Mask, at 8,000 hectares, is the sixth largest lake in Ireland the omission of any summary of its ornithological significance from an account of this nature might imply that the lake had never been properly surveyed. In fact, a number of aerial counts have been made of the entire lake, including a monthly series in winter 1972-73 and it is known to hold remarkably few birds for its size. During 1972-73 maximum counts were recorded for this large lake of 188 Mallard, 150 Teal, 120 Wigeon, 153 Tufted Duck, 43 Pochard and 28 Goldeneye.

Blacksod Bay

The north-west Mayo coast holds remarkably few waders in its numerous inlets. Blacksod Bay, between the southern arm of the Mullet peninsula and the mainland (Fig 17), is probably the most important of these bays. In autumn it holds several hundred Oystercatchers, up to 650 Ringed Plover and 100-200 each of Curlew, Bar-tailed Godwits, Redshanks, Dunlin and Sanderling. Numbers appear to be slightly lower in winter, but very little data is available on the area. In winter there are up to 150 Brent Geese.

Inishkea Islands

The Inishkea Islands are two low, windswept and now uninhabited islands situated some five kilometres off the Mullet peninsula (Fig. 17). Cattle and sheep are grazed on the sward which cover the islands.

The islands are of international importance as a haunt of Barnacle Geese. Cabot and West (1973) have emphasised the significance of these small islands as the winter haunt of up to 60% of the Irish Barnacle Goose wintering population. Counts of up to 2,900 have been recorded.

Both islands are the subject of an annual no-shooting Order.

Killala Bay

Killala Bay is a large triangular bay on the north Mayo coast. Most of the inter-tidal mudflat is situated at the southern corner, where the Moy enters the sea, and around Bartragh Island, but there are smaller inlets at Rathfran Bay and Lackan Bay on the west side which also hold flocks of waders.

The most numerous wildfowl are Wigeon, of which up to 560 occur in winter, mostly between Bartragh Island and the mainland. Only small numbers of Mallard, Teal, Red-breasted Mergansers and Shelduck occur. The area is quite important for waders. In November 1972, 307 Oystercatchers, 1,429 Lapwing, 480 Golden Plover, 850 Curlew, 93 Bar-tailed Godwits, 250 Redshanks and 947 Dunlin were counted in the Moy estuary, together with a handful of Grey Plover and Greenshanks. The only species recorded in Rathfran Bay and Lackan Bay in numbers over 100 in the same month were Lapwing (400 in each day) and Golden Plover (2,200 in Lacken Bay).

It is important to emphasise again that the above accounts only deal with those wetlands which have been counted. There is no doubt that a large number of other areas, particularly turloughs of importance for wild swans, have been omitted from the text because of our present inadequate state of knowledge.

NORTH-WEST

The north-west in this chapter comprises central and east Sligo, north Leitrim and Cavan, north Roscommon, almost all Fermanagh, west Tyrone and Donegal (Fig. 18). Fermanagh and west Tyrone are in Northern Ireland; the remainder of the area is in the Republic of Ireland.

The coast, like that of Connemara, is deeply indented, but most of the inlets are small or deep with stony or rocky edges. The smaller bays, such as Gweebarra Bay and Ballyness Bay, do hold flocks of ducks and waders, and some of them hold Brent Geese, but the numbers are much smaller than at Lough Swilly and the inlets in Sligo Bay. Like the Connemara coastal wetlands, these too have not been adequately studied and a great deal more work is required before really firm conclusions can be drawn.

Structurally the north-west is a complex area. Much of it is mountainous. In west Sligo the metamorphic Ox mountains, in south Sligo the Old Red sandstone Curlew mountains and in Donegal the schists, quartzites and granites of a number of ranges of differing ages dominate the landscape. Many of the inland wetlands are mountain lakes which hold very few waterfowl. However, carboniferous rocks, structurally part of the central lowlands, extend across Fermanagh and Leitrim to east Sligo and south Donegal. This area is drift covered and there are remarkable drumlin swarms in Leitrim, the Lough Erne basin, south-east of Sligo Bay and south of Donegal town. In this area there are a number of lakes close to sea-level, some of which hold quite large numbers of birds.

So far as is known the wetlands are not the subject of any particular threat at the moment.

Unfortunately, the literature on the birds of north-west Ireland is negligible. Perry (1975) dealt with the birds of a relatively small area, the Inishowen peninsula, and Deane (1954) in his work on the birds of Northern Ireland included records from the parts of Fermanagh and Tyrone which fall within this region. An additional difficulty for anyone writing on the birds of the area is the scarcity of skilled ornithologists living in the area or visiting it regularly. As a result, this chapter is probably more closely based on the wildfowl and wader counts carried out since 1966, and mostly since 1971, than any of the other chapters in this book.

Much the most numerous wintering duck in the north-west, as throughout most of the country, is the Wigeon. Numbers vary from month to month, but in most years a maximum of about 8,000 may be present, and there are indications that even larger numbers may sometimes be present in October.

Mallard and Teal are more difficult to estimate, but peak numbers are certainly somewhat less than this. Other species of duck are much scarcer. Greylag, White-fronted, Brent and Barnacle Geese all winter, but in quite small numbers. The area is extremely important for Whooper Swans, especially in October when birds make landfall here on their journey from Iceland. Over 2,000 probably occur in most years at this time of year. Mid-winter numbers are certainly lower, but probably exceed 1,000. Waders are not very numerous. Flocks of Lapwing and Golden Plover are not

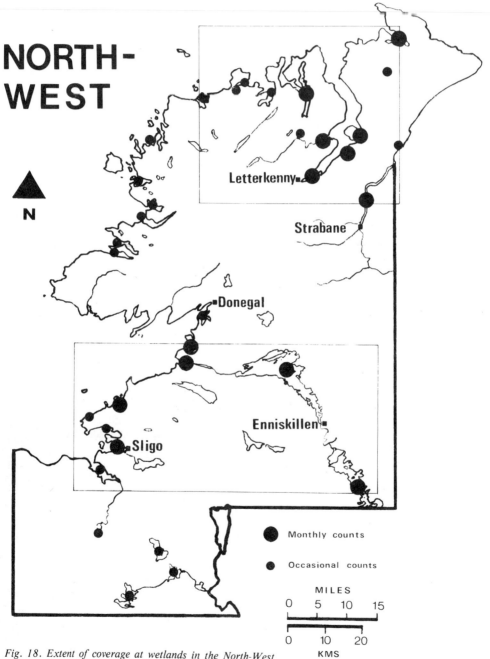

Fig. 18. Extent of coverage at wetlands in the North-West

so large as in the midlands, south and west, but are widespread. Curlew and Dunlin are perhaps the next most numerous waders.

The breeding population of Common Scoters on Lough Erne, which number 100-150 pairs (Sharrock 1976), represents much the largest colony in Britain and Ireland, and is probably the best known concentration of breeding ducks in the area. But a number of other species also breed. Mallard nest widely throughout the area; Teal breed quite widely throughout east Tyrone, west Fermanagh and south Donegal; Tufted Duck and Red-breasted Mergansers breed in the same area and also on the scattered lagoons along the north coast; Eiders nest on parts of the coast, but especially on islands, from Inishmurray, Co. Sligo northwards. Shelduck also nest around the coast and a pair of Goosanders has bred in Donegal since 1969.

A number of species of wader also nest in the region. Oystercatchers and Ringed Plover breed around the coastline; Lapwings breed in the lowlying parts and Golden Plover in mountainous parts. Snipe, Woodcock, Curlew and Common Sandpipers breed quite widely and Dunlin nest in a few areas, often in association with Golden Plover.

The small mountainous lakes of Donegal are the habitat of Ireland's few breeding Red-throated Divers. Great Crested Grebes nest in the Lough Erne system.

In dealing with the wetlands of the area the first sites discussed are those on the coast, working from Sligo Bay north and east to Malin Head. Then the inland wetlands are considered, working from south to north.

Sligo Bay

Sligo Bay is a broad bay which contains three estuaries, separated from each other by relatively narrow peninsulas (Fig. 19). Ballysadare Bay, the most southerly and the estuary of the Ballysadare river, is the longest and narrowest; Cummeen strand, the estuary of the Garavogue river and the central inlet, has the largest inter-tidal zone; Drumcliff Bay, the estuary of the Drumcliff river and the farthest north of these inlets, has inter-tidal mudflat and a pasture field to the north which is used by Barnacle Geese.

It seems likely that there is considerable movement of ducks and waders between these three estuaries, but no simultaneous counts have been made. Instead, our knowledge of the birds of the area is based on a series of counts carried out at irregular intervals at each of the three main estuaries.

Ballysadare holds several hundred ducks and varying numbers of waders, though they probably number more than 1,000 in total. Teal and Wigeon are much the most numerous ducks (up to 200 of each occur), though small parties of Mallard, Pintail, Red-breasted Mergansers and Shelduck also occur. Geese are rare and only a few swans are seen. By far the most common waders are Dunlin (up to 800). Up to 200 Curlew and Bar-tailed Godwits occur, and small numbers of Oystercatchers and Redshanks (less than 100 each).

Cummeen strand is far more important. In late September and October very large flocks of Wigeon and Brent Geese appear. The Brent Geese, which can number over 2,000 for a few weeks, a flock of international importance, move on quickly and by December only a couple of hundred remain. Wigeon also number 2,000 at times, but they decline to several hundred by December. The only other wildfowl which occur commonly on Cummeen strand are Mallard, which sometimes number several

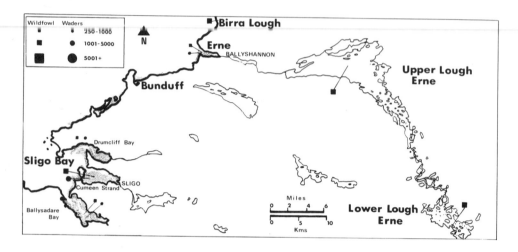

Fig. 19. Principal concentration of wildfowl and waders in Sligo and Fermanagh

hundred, but normally far less. This is the best wader area in Sligo Bay and the most numerous species are Oystercatcher (up to 700 in late autumn), Ringed Plover (up to 200), Curlew (up to 300), Bar-tailed Godwit (up to 180), Redshank (up to 160) and Dunlin (up to 200).

Drumcliff Bay to the north is best known for the flock of 300-600 Barnacle Geese (750 in 1976-77 and 1977-78) which winter in a field near Lissadell. This field is now a Forest and Wildlife sanctuary and is managed in the interests of the birds. Numbers have increased steadily over the past five years. The inter-tidal zone in the bay provides feeding for up to 200 ducks, most of which are Wigeon. The area holds up to 200 Oystercatchers and very small numbers of other waders.

Bunduff

North of Sligo, just west of the road to Bundoran, lies the small Bunduff lake (Fig. 19). The lake and surrounding fields hold populations of up to 80 White-fronted Geese and up to 40 Whooper Swans. Small numbers of both dabbling and diving ducks also occur.

Erne Estuary

The estuary of the Erne river, between Ballyshannon and the sea (Fig. 19) holds small numbers of Mallard, Teal, Wigeon, Goldeneye, Common Scoters and Red-breasted Mergansers. Rarely are more than 90 of any of these species counted. A scattering of most of the common Irish waders occurs on passage and in winter. Oystercatchers, the most numerous waders, number up to 180 in autumn, but less than 100 in winter. Dunlin are the next most common waders, but number only 150 or so in winter.

Birra Lough

Birra Lough is a shallow freshwater lake with extensive reed-beds close to Rossnowlagh, between Ballyshannon and Donegal town (Fig. 19). It is one of Ireland's great Whooper Swan haunts. Numbers fluctuate considerably from year to year and even from day to day, but it is quite usual for 200 to be present. Large numbers of Mute Swans also occur (up to 150), but Bewick's Swans are quite rare. The lake also has a population of several hundred dabbling ducks, mostly Mallard, Teal and Wigeon, and somewhat similar numbers of diving ducks, mostly Pochard. Very few waders are present.

Donegal Bay

Donegal Bay is quite an extensive complex of small inlets and bays. Very few wildfowl occur, but close to 1,000 waders have been counted. Oystercatchers (up to 100), Curlew (up to 250) and Dunlin (up to 250) appear to be the most numerous species. Out in the bay Common Scoters winter. A small flock of Brent Geese (up to 150) visits the area in late winter.

Loughros Bay, Gweebarra Bay and Clooney Lake

Loughros Bay and Gweebarra Bay, on the west coast of Donegal, have inter-tidal mudflats which hold small numbers of waders, chiefly Oystercatchers (up to 200) and Curlews (up to 300). Small numbers of Brent Geese (up to 50) winter in Gweebarra Bay and a small party of Long-tailed Ducks (up to 30) is usually to be seen off Portnoo in winter. A small lake near Naran, Clooney Lake, holds small numbers of ducks. Pochard (50-120) are the most numerous.

Ballyness Bay

Ballyness Bay, a small muddy inlet between Bloody Foreland and Horn Head on the north coast of Donegal (Fig. 20), holds small flocks of Mallard (up to 100), Wigeon (up to 200) and Brent Geese (up to 140) in late autumn and winter. Numbers of waders are low, with Oystercatchers (up to 100 in autumn, 50 in winter), Curlew (up to 200) and Dunlin (up to 200 in autumn) the most numerous. Large numbers of Ringed Plover (340) and Sanderling (190) have been recorded in September.

Dunfanaghy

The New Lake and small tidal inlet at Dunfanaghy (Fig. 20) south of Horn Head, support several hundred wildfowl and waders. The lake holds quite an important breeding population of Mallard and Tufted Duck. In winter up to 200 dabbling ducks, mostly Wigeon, and up to 250 diving ducks, mostly Tufted Duck and Pochard, occur. On the estuary, outside the lake, Oystercatchers (up to 90), Curlew (up to 200) and Redshanks (up to 20) occur. A flock of about 30 White-fronted Geese winters in the vicinity of the lake.

Sheep Haven

Sheep Haven is a broad bay in north Donegal (Fig. 20) with the estuary of the Lackagh river at its head. The bay is long and complex and waterfowl counts have only been made twice, in January 1969 and September 1970. In January 860 Wigeon and 102 Shelduck were counted, but only a handful of other ducks. No count was made of waders. In September the only duck found was one Red-breasted Merganser, but small numbers of Oystercatchers, Lapwing, Curlew and Dunlin were seen. The total count was only 160 waders. However, the large count of Wigeon in January 1969 suggests that the area should be further investigated.

Mulroy Bay

Mulroy Bay is a long, narrow inlet between Sheep Haven and Lough Swilly (Fig. 20). From seven waterfowl counts made at irregular intervals since January 1969 it is clear that the bay holds a regular winter population of 150-250 Wigeon and 50-150 Mute Swans, but other species of wildfowl are much scarcer. Wader numbers, as in most of the Donegal bays, are small with less than 60 each of Oystercatchers, Curlew and Redshanks wintering.

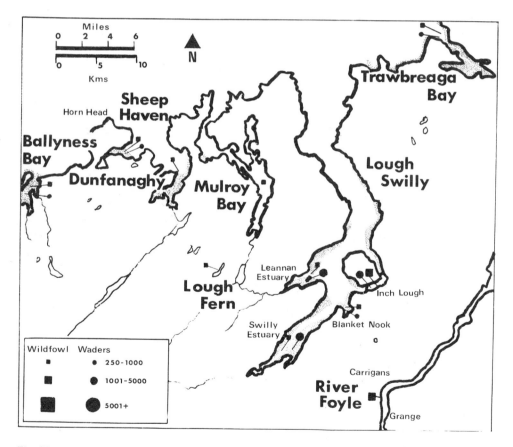

Fig. 20. Principal concentration of wildfowl and waders in north Donegal

Lough Swilly

Lough Swilly (Fig. 20) has much the finest coastal wetland habitat in Donegal. The lough, like Mulroy Bay to the east, is a long, thin inlet gouged out by glaciation, but on a much larger scale than the other bay. It runs for 50 kilometres from south to north and is no more than four kilometres wide at its broadest point. There are extensive inter-tidal mudflats and shingle banks in the southern half of the lough.

The most important sections for birds are the Leannan and Swilly estuaries and the man-made lagoons of Blanket Nook and Inch Lough, both on the east side of Lough Swilly. Blanket Nook is a small brackish inlet which was cut off by the construction of a dyke across its mouth. Inch Lough was formed by the construction of dykes at both ends of a channel between Inch Island and the mainland. The lake is only slightly brackish and there are some large reed-beds. In winter the lough floods quite extensively.

Lough Swilly is a complex area for the waterfowl counter and only three attempts have been made to assess the winter population of the entire area. These were in January 1969, September 1970 and December 1974, but waders were not counted in 1969. However, a large number of counts have been made at individual sections of the lough.

The lough is particularly important as a Whooper Swan haunt. Counts of up to 1,500 have been made in October, usually in fields near Inch Lough, but these have never been recorded as present for more than a few days. Normal winter numbers are in the region of 100-500 birds and the swans move about between Inch Lough, Blanket Nook and the small Port Lough near Newtown Cunningham. These figures indicate that the area is of real international importance for the species, a large proportion of the Icelandic breeding population appearing to make landfall there. The lough is of national importance for Greylag Geese. Up to 350 have been recorded at Inch, but the birds commute between this area and a five-kilometre stretch of the river Foyle south of Carrigans.

The entire lough is quite important for wildfowl and waders. In the two mid-winter counts of the entire lough maxima of 796 Mallard, 1,082 Teal, 1,444 Wigeon, 155 Pintail, 183 Shoveler, 101 Tufted Duck, 193 Pochard and 483 Shelduck were recorded as well as smaller numbers of other species of ducks. Wigeon numbers are certainly much higher in autumn: 1,600 have been counted in Blanket Nook and at Inch Lough alone in late September. A small number of Brent Geese (less than 100) winter on the shore of Inch Island and some White-fronted Geese sometimes occur on the lough. A large flock of Mute Swans (up to 200) winters at Inch Lough.

Lough Swilly has a similar population of waders to the other Donegal estuaries and bays, though numbers are considerably larger. Yet, both the numbers and diversity of waders are poor when compared with east and south coast wetlands. Mid-winter totals of 517 Oystercatchers, 800 Lapwing, 860 Curlew, 525 Redshanks and 2,000 Dunlin are very high, however, for the north-west and there is evidence that much larger numbers of Redshanks occur sometimes in late autumn.

Blanket Nook is protected by an annual no-shooting Order.

Lough Erne

The Lough Erne basin comprises two lakes, Upper and Lower Lough Erne, each of which has numerous islands and peninsulas. In effect the lakes form a large area of water between drumlins and low hills. Around the lakes is a network of boggy and marshy land in which smaller lakes are situated. The system is really a continuation of the complex of lakes in the Republic through which the Erne river flows — Loughs Gowna and Oughter — which have already been discussed.

Since the Erne lakes are so complicated they are very difficult to count. This summary is based on counts carried out in 1967-68 and 1968-69 and particularly on an assessment of the total number of wildfowl occurring on the lakes in winter prepared after the first winter's counts (Curran 1968). These probably provide a better guide to the potential of the area than the actual counts which are incomplete. Unfortunately, there appear to be no recent counts available for the area.

Lower Lough Erne is principally important for its breeding population of Common Scoters which number between 100 and 150 pairs (Ferguson 1968, 1971). In winter the Lower Lough has a large grebe population, estimated at 50-150 Great Crested and 100-300 Little Grebes. Dabbling ducks are relatively scarce, though small numbers of Mallard (perhaps up to 250), Teal (up to 50), and Wigeon (up to 200) occur. The area is more important for diving ducks and the population of Tufted Ducks (800-1,000), Pochard (200-300), Goldeneye (50-100) and Red-breasted Mergansers (10-100) can be quite large. Small numbers of Mute and Whooper Swans also winter and, of course, there are Coots (250-500).

The estimates of populations on the Upper Lough indicate a similar winter population of Great Crested Grebes and diving ducks, except for Goldeneye and Red-breasted Mergansers which are much scarcer. Dabbling ducks, however, are more numerous. Estimates of 250-500 Mallard, 300-650 Teal, 250-500 Wigeon, 10-100 Pintail and 100-250 Shoveler indicate quite a healthy winter population of surface-feeders. There is also a small wintering flock of White-fronted Geese (up to 60) in the area. Smaller numbers of Mute Swans occur, but Whooper Swans appear to be much more numerous. In 1968-69 a maximum of 156 was counted in February. Cabot (1967) counted 525 wild swans from the air in January on Upper Lough Erne.

The Royal Society for the Protection of Birds has a bird reserve at Castle Caldwell.

Trawbreaga Bay

Trawbreaga Bay is Ireland's most northerly wetland (Fig. 20), a broad bay with a narrow exit a few kilometres south of Malin Head. In summer Eiders nest in the area. In winter it is a haunt of Brent Geese (70-240) and Barnacle Geese (70-200). Quite large numbers of ducks occur. Up to 180 Mallard in autumn and 180 Wigeon in winter are regular and large flocks of Teal have also been recorded. Waders are also relatively numerous with up to 200 Oystercatchers and 350 Curlew the most abundant.

West shore of Lough Foyle

The west shore of Lough Foyle is not included in the detailed counts of the lough carried out by the Route Naturalists' Field Club. Almost certainly this omission does not cause any significant error for the shore from Muff to Quigley's Point holds only a few Mallard, Teal, Wigeon and Shelduck (up to 200 in total) and occasionally a few hundred Lapwing and Dunlin.

Lough Gara

Lough Gara is a medium-sized lake on the Boyle River upstream of Lough Key. The lake is divided into a large northern section and a small southern section with a narrow inter-connecting channel.

The lake is very important for White-fronted Geese, holding one of the largest flocks in the country away from the Wexford Slobs. Peak numbers in January are about 300 birds. The geese frequent fields on an island in the lake and in the vicinity of the lake. The lake itself is also important for other wildfowl. Up to 260 Mallard, 600 Teal, 600 Wigeon, 50 Tufted Duck, 900 Pochard, 120 Mute Swans and 140 Whooper Swans occur in autumn and winter.

Part of the lake is the subject of a no-shooting Order.

Lough Arrow

Lough Arrow is quite a large lake (1,250 hectares) and holds considerable numbers of grebes, diving ducks and Coots. Counts of over 60 Little Grebes have been made on several occasions and 200 Tufted Duck, 480 Pochard and 570 Coots have been recorded. Dabbling ducks are very irregular.

Templehouse Lough

Templehouse Lough is a small, shallow lake (140 hectares) situated near Ballymote in Sligo and surrounded by a large expanse of moorland. The lake holds a large Mallard population (up to 450) and quite large numbers of Teal (up to 100), Wigeon (up to 180), Tufted Duck (up to 70) and Goldeneye (up to 40). White-fronted Geese and wild swans occur occasionally in winter. This lake deserves further study.

River Foyle

The stretch of the river Foyle which runs between Grange, on the Derry side, and Saint Johnstown and Carrigans on the Donegal side is very important for ducks, geese and swans. The river is tidal at this point and there are rough pasture fields on both sides.

This is one of Ireland's best goose haunts, but the Greylag and White-fronted Geese which winter here also move across to Inch Lough and Blanket Nook on Lough Swilly and north to the shore of Lough Foyle. However, 100-180 Greylag Geese and 90-300 White-fronted Geese are regularly counted in the area, most often being seen on the Derry side of the river. The site is also a good dabbling duck and wild swan haunt. Mid-winter counts of 400-1,000 Mallard, 150-1,000 Teal and 50-400 Wigeon indicate that the area is a very important Mallard haunt and, at times, important for Teal. Wild swans, usually Whooper Swans, occur mostly in fields in the Grange area. Numbers are highest in autumn (up to 350) but decline in winter. These birds also commute to Lough Swilly.

Wader numbers are low apart from flocks of several hundred Lapwing, Golden Plover and Curlew.

Lough Fern

Lough Fern is a medium-sized lake situated directly south of Mulroy Bay. Not many dabbling ducks winter on the lake. Though flocks of 200 Mallard and 150 Teal have been recorded numbers are normally much lower. Very large numbers of diving ducks can occur and it is of interest that the largest count of Pochard was 1,100 in late September in 1974. By February none remained. The second largest count was 550 in October in the previous year, but by December there were only 124. This pattern suggests that Lough Fern, like Loughs Corrib, Cullin and Derravaragh, may act as a focal point for arriving Pochard in autumn. However, such large numbers do not always occur: in autumn 1972 the maximum recorded was 162 in late September. Numbers of Tufted Duck are lower, the highest count recorded being 250.

G.D.A.

NORTH AND NORTH-EAST

This region comprises most of Northern Ireland and includes all its important wetlands with the exceptions of the north shore of Carlingford Lough, the Lough Erne system and the east bank of the River Foyle at Grange. It includes Londonderry, Antrim, Down, Armagh and east Tyrone.

The coast is marked by three major indentations — Lough Foyle, Belfast Lough and Strangford Lough. Between these sea-loughs much of the coast is high, particularly in Antrim and south Down, and there are very few inlets of importance for wetland birds, the Bann Estuary, Larne Lough and Dundrum Bay being the only exceptions.

Inland the dominating wetland, indeed one of the dominant physical features of Northern Ireland, is Lough Neagh, here taken to include Lough Beg which is immediately to its north-west. The lough is surrounded by a low shoreline and, as few roads run beside it, the enormous expanse of water is not as obvious to the visitor as would be imagined from a study of the map. Lough Neagh is situated in a depression in the basaltic plateau which extends over much of north-east Northern Ireland. South and south-east of Lough Neagh are gravels and clays which indicate a considerable amount of infill on the margins of what was formerly a much more extensive lake.

The basalts outcrop on the coast from north Londonderry to Cave Hill overlooking Belfast in a series of great cliffs; several lava flows may be distinguished at many sites including the most noteworthy location of the Giant's Causeway. The mass of lava is extraordinarily deep; a borehole near Lough Neagh showed a thickness approaching 800 metres (Whittow 1974).

Around Lough Foyle the land is low and flat between the basalt cliffs and the shore. This expanse, consisting of a series of broad terraces, represents several post-glacial raised shorelines. Further south the land is higher and dominated by the schists, grits and igneous rocks of the Sperrin Mountains.

South of the Antrim Plateau and the Lagan Valley the land is generally low to the Mountains of Mourne, the landscape being dominated by drumlins. In the poorly-drained depressions between the drumlins are lakes, or bogs, in many cases now drained for agricultural purposes. The southern part of this region includes the Mourne Mountains, in whose slate and granite hills virtually the only wetlands are a few corrie lakes and three large artificial reservoirs.

Despite Northern Ireland being a well-watched region, the ornithological literature is sparse. The standard work on its birds (Deane 1954) is now much out of date. However, students at the New University of Ulster produced a bird report covering much of north Londonderry and Antrim for 1970 and 1971; these were updated to a review of the status of the birds of the area by Marsh (1975). Recently a book has been published dealing with the birds of Lough Beg (D'Arcy 1978). Otherwise the principal sources of data are the series of duplicated reports on the wildfowl counts undertaken by the Northern Ireland Ornithologists' Club at Lough Neagh from 1965 to 1969 and at the sea-loughs (excluding Strangford and Belfast Loughs) in 1972-73 and 1973-74 and the wildfowl and wader counts carried out by the National Trust Strangford

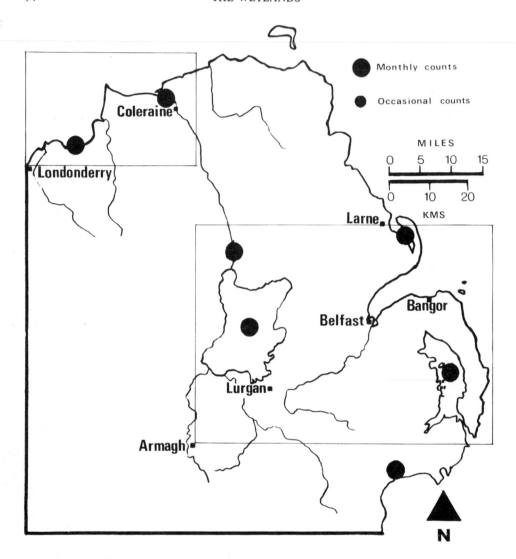

Monthly counts

Occasional counts

MILES

0   5   10   15

0   10   20

KMS

Coleraine

Londonderry

Larne

Bangor

Belfast

Lurgan

Armagh

N

NORTH & NORTH-EAST

Fig. 21. Extent of coverage at wetlands in the North and North-East

Lough Wildlife Scheme and the Route Naturalists' Field Club at Strangford Lough and Lough Foyle respectively since the mid-1960s.

The most numerous ducks in the region are Wigeon (up to 30,000 in autumn),

Tufted Duck (up to 29,000 on Lough Neagh) and Pochard (up to 37,000 on Lough Neagh). Goldeneye (up to 6,000) are also numerous on Lough Neagh. Counts of over 1,000 Mute Swans have been made on Lough Neagh in autumn, and the other two swan species each numbered several hundred during the years of the counts. The most abundant waders are Knot and Dunlin which concentrate in their largest numbers on Strangford Lough. Counts of each vary enormously, but up to 30,000 Knot and 15,000 Dunlin have been recorded. Lapwing and Curlew are also numerous, but feed inland on fields in large numbers and wetland figures do not represent the true level of the population.

Large numbers of ducks and grebes nest in this part of Ireland. Mallard, Teal, Tufted Duck, Red-breasted Mergansers and Shelduck are the most widespread, but Eiders nest around the coast and several Shoveler breed, mostly around Lough Neagh. This lake also attracts rare breeding ducks including Garganey (occasionally), Gadwall, Pintail and Pochard and has the largest concentration of Great Crested Grebes in Ireland. Breeding waders are not so abundant as wildfowl, though Lapwing, Snipe and Curlew breed widely. Woodcock, Redshanks and Common Sandpipers are more thinly distributed and Golden Plover are scarce and most often encountered in Antrim. Dunlin are rare, but a few breed in the Lough Neagh basin and perhaps on the Antrim plateau. The Oystercatcher is probably the most numerous coastal breeding wader. Ringed Plover, while widespread, are not common; a census in Northern Ireland in 1975 resulted in a total of only 93 pairs with the largest numbers (50 pairs) in Strangford Lough (Prater 1976).

The first wetlands to be discussed are those on the coast, working clockwise from Lough Foyle to Dundrum Bay, and then Lough Neagh and its enormous wildfowl populations are considered.

Lough Foyle

Lough Foyle is a broad sea-lough with extensive inter-tidal mud-flats on its southern and eastern rims. At several places behind the inter-tidal zone there are hundreds of hectares of alluvial land reclaimed from the sea in the nineteenth century and most of the bay itself is very shallow.

The data on which this account of the birds is based consist of wildfowl counts by the Northern Ireland Ornithologists' Club for 1972-73 and 1973-74, waterfowl counts by the Route Naturalists' Field Club for the years from 1966-67 to 1971-72 and Marsh's (1975) account of the birds of the north coast.

Unfortunately, there have been differences of opinion as to the number of wildfowl using this huge area, but it is quite clear that enormous numbers of Wigeon occur in October, peak counts ranging from 10,000 to 29,000. Numbers in mid-winter are much lower, ranging about 3,000, but as an autumn passage site Lough Foyle is of international importance. The populations of Mallard (up to 2,000) and Pintail (up to 450) are of national importance. Both Greylag and White-fronted Geese were once regular winter visitors in flocks of 200-400 birds to the Donnybrewer/Longfield Intake, but visits of only a few birds are now rather spasmodic. Brent Geese, however, frequently occur in numbers up to 500 on passage in September and October; smaller parties may be seen later in the season. The area is of international importance for wild swans, which feed largely on the reclaimed land. Whooper Swans usually number 300-

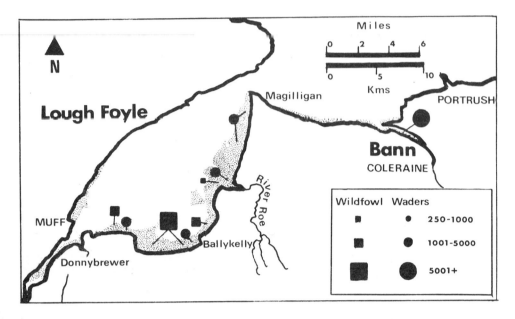

Fig. 22. Principal concentrations of wildfowl and waders at Lough Foyle and the Bann Estuary

500, but the numbers of Bewick's Swans fluctuate considerably. In 1971-72 as many as 1,059 were counted, but numbers are more usually in the region of 100-200.

Lough Foyle is the second most important wader haunt in the area (Table 25) though the wader counts included in the total are extremely conservative, because of the difficulty of counting such a wide bay and the number of waders which feed up to two kilometres inland, and actual totals may be appreciably higher. The area is of importance chiefly for large waders and, according to Marsh (1975), holds up to 4,000 Oystercatchers, 10,000 Lapwing, 8,000 Golden Plover, 2,000 Curlew (but over 5,000 have been recorded at an evening roost in autumn), 3,000 Bar-tailed Godwits, 1,500 Redshanks and over 2,500 Dunlin. The figures for Curlew, Bar-tailed Godwits and Redshanks qualify the Lough as a site of international importance.

The only special protection given in the area is a National Nature Reserve at the important wader site of the Roe Estuary.

Bann

The Bann estuary (Fig. 22) is a long, narrow estuary running from Coleraine north-westwards to the sea. It is bounded by sand dunes and farmland, and has only a relatively small area of tidal marsh. Numbers of ducks are very low but the area is the third most important wader site in Northern Ireland (Table 25). However, the most numerous birds are Lapwing (up to 6,000), Golden Plover (up to 2,400) and Curlew (up to 1,000), none of which are exclusively shorebirds. In autumn Redshanks number up to 300 and Dunlin up to 450, emphasising the significance of the site for passage migrants. An area near the sea is managed as a wildlife refuge by the National Trust.

Larne Lough

Larne Lough (Fig. 23) is long and almost enclosed; it has extensive mudflats and a very restricted area of saltmarsh. The lough holds good numbers of duck particularly Teal (up to 600), Wigeon (up to 2,000), and Shelduck (up to 270). The concentration of up to 50 Goldeneye is quite large for a sea-lough. Brent Geese winter in numbers between 80 and 100. It is the fourth most important wader haunt in Northern Ireland (Table 25) but the most numerous species is the Lapwing which peaks at 2,000-2,600 birds each winter. The commonest shore wader is the Redshank (peak of 600-800) and Oystercatchers, Curlew and Dunlin each number between 200 and 600 at their peak in winter. Land reclamation works and the disposal of quarry overburden have resulted in the reduction of its importance generally. There is one Statutory Bird Sanctuary at the upstream end of the lough.

Belfast Lough

The birds of Belfast Lough have not been assessed in recent years; land reclamation works, the denial of access to certain significant areas for security reasons, and the troubled conditions pertaining in parts of Belfast have all contributed to this unfortunate situation. It is to be doubly regretted in that the effects of the reclamation works have not been recorded, and there are no baselines on which to base evidence of any changes which will result from the construction of a major power station, the water waste from which will probably enter the Lough at a higher temperature than the Lough.

Strangford Lough

Strangford Lough is a large and almost completely land-locked sea-lough (Fig. 23) with a deeply indented coastline more than 130 kilometres in length, but with an outlet channel to the Irish Sea of only 800 metres width. Tidal mudflats are extensive, especially so at the northern end of the Lough; elsewhere shorelines are rocky. No major rivers enter the Lough, with the exception of the Quoile, which in 1957 had a barrage constructed across its mouth to form a large freshwater pondage to assist with the alleviation of drainage problems. There are some areas of saltings and saltmarsh. As well as having a complex coastline, the Lough has a great many islands, the result of drumlins being drowned by the sea.

The National Trust owns or leases virtually all of the shoreline, and, in conjunction with local landowners, wildfowlers and ornithologists, organises regular counts of the area. However, the method of counting, which involves a large number of counters each covering small sections of the Lough, carries considerable risks in omitting or duplicating counts of flocks. Also, birds may be missed if they are on any of the many lakes within five kilometres of the Lough.

Nevertheless, counts of the Lough indicate that it is extremely important for wildfowl, particularly in the autumn. Counts of over 10,000 Brent Geese, some 60%-70% of the Irish wintering population, have been made on a number of occasions. Peak counts of Wigeon have ranged between 6,600 and 20,400 in the four years from 1971-72 to 1974-75, and of Shelduck between 1,100 and 1,600. Both of these species occur in internationally important numbers, as do the 400-600 Whooper Swans which winter in the area. The populations of Pintail (200-600) and Red-breasted Mergansers (300-500) are of national importance.

The Lough is much the most important wader haunt in Northern Ireland (Table 25). Taken with Dundalk Bay and the Shannon Estuary this area is one of the top three Irish estuaries for waders. The most numerous are Oystercatchers (up to 3,000), Lapwing (up to 13,000), Curlew (up to 3,000), Bar-tailed Godwits (up to 1,700), Redshanks (up to 2,000), Knot (12,000-30,000) and Dunlins (up to 10,000). The populations of Curlew, Bar-tailed Godwits, Redshanks and Knot are of international importance, and those of Oystercatchers and Dunlin of national importance. Indeed, the Knot concentration is much the biggest in Ireland. There are no accepted criteria for defining the significance of Lapwing numbers, but the Strangford flocks must be among the largest in Europe.

Although both ducks and waders are widely distributed around the Lough, the largest concentrations of each are found in the northern third of the area, from Mahee Island around to Greyabbey Bay.

The National Trust, in co-operation with wildfowlers' organisations, landowners and ornithologists, administers the highly successful Strangford Lough Wildlife

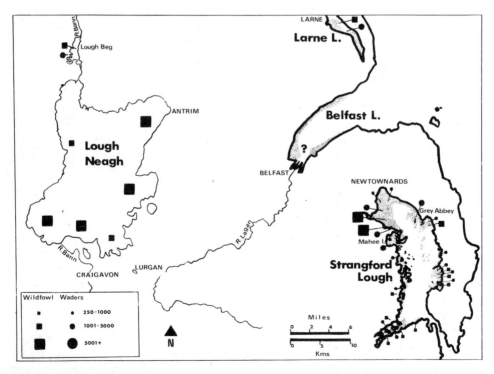

Fig. 23. Principal concentrations of wildfowl and waders in north-east Ireland

Table 25

Maximum numbers of waders recorded at estuaries in north-east Ireland, 1971-72 to 1974-75 (source Prater 1973a, 1974a, 1976a, 1978). No data are available for Belfast Lough

	1971-72	1972-73	1973-74	1974-75
Strangford Lough	49,000	29,900	62,400	28,300
Lough Foyle	16,300	22,900	14,100	19,900
Bann Estuary	7,600	5,800	8,300	6,500
Larne Lough	4,500	4,600	3,800	2,800
Dundrum Bay	1,800	2,200	2,600	3,200

Scheme. Under this scheme, permits are required to shoot on the open areas, while there are six major refuges where birds must not be disturbed. Certain favoured nesting islands are also denied to public access. The Quoile Pondage is a National Nature Reserve, and in addition, some of the islands jointly form a Statutory Bird Sanctuary.

Dundrum Bay

Dundrum Bay is a broad and relatively shallow bay, partly surrounded by sand dunes, and with a smaller, narrower inner bay which has extensive mudflats.

The bay holds an interesting duck population with 300-600 Wigeon and small numbers of Mallard in the Inner Bay, and fluctuating numbers of Common Scoters (200-1,300) and Red-breasted Mergansers (30-200) in the outer bay.

Numbers of waders are quite low in total (Table 25) but include relatively few Lapwing and Golden Plover. Peaks of 400-600 Oystercatchers 200-400 Redshanks and 500-800 Dunlin indicate that the bay is quite important for shore waders.

Lough Neagh

Lough Neagh (Fig. 23) is the largest body of freshwater in Ireland and Britain, covering an area of 250 square kilometres. Set in a depression in the basalts, a succession of lowerings of the water level, the last in 1959, have considerably altered the shoreline. Where resulting shores are extensive, such as on the south shore, the land has been used for agricultural purposes, but in many stretches natural processes of recolonisation have not been stopped, thus allowing scub growth, fen development, or appearance of reedswamp. There are many expanses of lowland peat bog in the 10 kilometres behind the lough, particularly to the south. Several islands exist, ranging from some with mature woodland to recently exposed low rocky flats. Six major rivers enter Lough Neagh, the outlet from which, the Lower Bann, is at the north-west corner. Two kilometres to the north-west is Lough Beg, whose west shore is meadow, frequently flooded during winter; the east shore is a series of bays, some colonised by reedswamp or fen. Ornithologically it is very rich, with its many food-rich habitats; like Lough Neagh it is extremely shallow, but the underwater vegetation is much richer than in the larger lough.

For the purposes of the remainder of this section Lough Neagh is taken to include Lough Beg.

Lough Neagh is one of Europe's most important wildfowl haunts, and holds many more duck at all seasons than any other Irish site. The winter populations of Teal, Pintail, Shoveler, Tufted Duck, Pochard, Goldeneye, Whooper Swans and Bewick's

Swans (Table 26) are regularly of international importance and those of Mallard, Scaup and Mute Swans occasionally so. The lough is of exceptional importance for diving ducks. Only two individual sites in north-west Europe hold more Tufted Duck, one on the Baltic coast of Denmark and the other in the south-east Ijsselmeer in the Netherlands. Similarly, only two sites, one the south-east Ijsselmeer in the nearby on the Dutch coast, hold more Pochard (Atkinson-Willes 1976).

In summer over 1,000 pairs of Tufted Duck nest, together with smaller numbers of Teal, Shoveler, Red-breasted Mergansers and Shelduck, and a few Gadwall, Pintail and, perhaps, Garganey. Up to 50 Goldeneye are regularly present during the summer, and occasionally Scaup and Common Scoters. The breeding population of Mute Swans is very large: each autumn from 1966 to 1968 the number of immatures counted exceeded 100 and ranged from 118 to 273.

Ducks are widely distributed around the Lough, but the largest concentrations of surface-feeding ducks, swans and Coots are normally at Lough Beg.

Complete protection for wildfowl is afforded at the various nature reserves around the area and there are two large Statutory Wildfowl Refuges. In addition, wildfowlers manage a number of small refuges, and also a major refuge on Lough Beg. The area is designated as a Wetland of International Importance under the 'Ramsar' Convention.

The wetland has not been counted since 1969; despite the physical difficulties involved in such an operation it is highly desirable that up-to-date information is obtained as frequently as possible.

Table 26

Peak counts of wildfowl at Lough Neagh, 1964-65 to 1968-69

	1964-65	1965-66	1966-67	1967-68	1968-69
Mallard	2,100	5,400	10,700	7,300	7,000
Teal	3,500	2,600	2,600	2,900	1,800
Wigeon	3,000	2,100	2,100	4,300	1,700
Pintail	1,000	600	600	700	100
Shoveler	400	300	200	600	300
Scaup	1,100	500	1,000	2,200	2,200
Tufted Duck	18,000	30,400	17,600	28,900	25,700
Pochard	14,200	37,600	11,300	11,700	14,500
Goldeneye	3,500	4,800	5,700	5,400	3,200
Shelduck	300	100	200	200	100
Mute Swan	700	1,000	1,200	1,200	1,200
Whooper Swan	600	800	500	700	400
Bewick's Swan	500	400	500	200	300
Coot	2,300	4,100	3,300	3,400	4,400
Number of months counted	3	9	12	10	6

THE BIRDS

DUCKS

Ducks are the birds most immediately associated with wetlands by the layman. Geese and even swans will graze quite far from water; waders occur on fields and on the edges of water; but ducks spend most of their lives actually on the water. They are easily recognised by their dumpy bodies, short necks and webbed feet. A total of 30 species has occurred in Ireland, but 15 of these are rare visitors from Europe, North America and, in one case, Asia. The 15 commoner species fall into four main taxonomic divisions.

The best known ducks, because they are the quarry of shooting men, are the dabbling ducks, so called because they feed by dabbling on the surface of the water. The common Irish species are the Mallard, Teal, Gadwall, Wigeon, Pintail and Shoveler. Mallard, Teal, Gadwall and Pintail also feed by upending, Pintail, which have longer necks, often in slightly deeper water. Wigeon are primarily grazing ducks, and Pintail, where they occur inland, appear to feed largely by grazing also. The Shoveler has a feeding technique of its own. Its broad bill has very fine projections which form a mesh along the side. Water is sucked in at the tip of the bill and then squirted out through this filter, the food items being retained. Although each of these species has been recorded nesting in Ireland, only Mallard do so abundantly and Gadwall, Wigeon and Pintail are extremely rare breeders. Apart from Mallard, which are mainly sedentary, most of the dabbling ducks on Irish wetlands in winter are immigrants from Iceland, Scotland, Scandinavia, Russia and central Europe.

There are three relatively common diving duck species wintering in Ireland, the Tufted Duck, Pochard and Scaup. The first two are birds of lakes and broad rivers, the last is found mainly on the sea and is not a typical wetland species. Each of these species feeds by diving. Tufted Duck and Scaup are largely animal feeders, the large bill of the Scaup being well adapted to feeding on shellfish, and Pochard are vegetarian. Tufted Duck are now common breeding birds in Ireland; Pochard are rare; Scaup have never been recorded breeding here. The bulk of the winter population of the first two species is comprised of immigrants and obviously all the Scaup are foreign breeders.

A number of species are classified as sea ducks, Two of these, the Goldeneye and Red-breasted Merganser, are common wetland species in Ireland; three, the Long-tailed Duck, Common Scoter and Eider, are birds of deeper, coastal waters. All of them obtain their food by diving. We know very little about the food of the Goldeneye, but Red-breasted Mergansers are almost exclusively fish eaters. Long-tailed Duck, Common Scoters and Eiders feed on molluscs and crustaceans, though Common Scoters are particularly dependent on mussels. Red-breasted Mergansers and Eiders, which breed in Ireland, are apparently sedentary. Some Common Scoters breed in the north-west, but the majority of those seen around the coast are immigrants. The other species are exclusively visitors to Ireland outside the breeding season.

The final category has only one species, the Shelduck. This is a much larger, more goose-like duck than any of the others. It feeds largely on estuaries where its main prey item, the marine mollusc, *Hydrobia ulvae*, lives in abundance.

The history of wildfowl counting in Ireland has been outlined in the Introduction. At the commencement of the *Wetlands Enquiry* in 1971-72 we knew from the international counts we had been participating in where the most important wetlands for duck were located and we knew the approximate number of birds which could occur on most of them in January. But we knew very little about the times of arrival and departure; we did not know whether some wetlands which were relatively unimportant in mid-winter held large numbers of birds at other times of the year; we knew virtually nothing of the birds of the entire Shannon system; we had little idea how many ducks of any species occurred in Ireland in mid-winter. After four winters of monthly counts our knowledge is vastly increased. We know when most duck arrive and depart; we know that some wetlands are extremely important for ducks in autumn and spring but less so in January; our knowledge of particular areas, such as Dundalk Bay and the Shannon system from Lough Allen to the sea, is greatly extended. We can even make a reasonable estimate of the numbers of most species of duck wintering in Ireland.

In the pages which follow, the information on duck numbers and distribution is presented, mainly on maps, but occasionally in graphs or tables. The aim has been to show the Irish distribution simply and to discuss it in the context of the north-west European population of each species. All the data on the maps are based on counts made between 1971-72 and 1974-75 except for those sites indicated by stippling. Earlier data, whether from special surveys such as the Lough Neagh counts or from the international duck counts, have been used for those areas in the absence of up-to-date information. The information presented on the maps showing the number of birds occurring at each site is based on the average count during the relevant period.

So, what is Ireland's significance for ducks? As a breeding area it is clearly not very important. As a wintering area in normal circumstances it holds a reasonably large proportion of the ducks which migrate across the north-west European flyway. Ireland holds more than 10% of the north-west European wintering population of four species: Teal (20%-30%), Wigeon (20%-25%), Shoveler (20%) and Pochard (possibly up to 15%). Ireland is particularly important for Teal as the most westerly extension of the winter range of a species which is particularly susceptible to cold weather and for Wigeon as the wintering area of much of the Icelandic breeding population. These are species particularly dependent in Ireland on turloughs and callows around the Shannon and its tributaries and farther west, habitats which are coming under increasing threat from drainage. But in the occasional very hard winters which grip Europe for weeks on end Ireland may be much more important for the ducks which fly west as the temperature falls. Ringing recoveries in January 1963 showed that many ducks moved to Ireland ahead of the cold weather, but unfortunately there was no system of duck counts in existence then. Nor have we had a sufficiently cold winter since 1971-72 to demonstrate the importance of Ireland as a refuge, but the duck counters are all waiting for the next hard winter to quantify the immigration.

Mallard *Anas platyrhynchos*

The Mallard or Wild Duck is probably the most familiar duck in Ireland, occurring on virtually every lake, river, estuary, marsh, bog and pond in the country. The drake is a handsome bird with a pale grey body and dark chestnut breast separated by a thin white collar from a dark green head which sometimes shows a purple sheen. The duck is a drab, mottled brown rather like most other female ducks. Both can be distinguished with practice by their characteristic large size and upright carriage when on the water, and their dark blue speculum in flight.

Mallard breed throughout Europe, Asia and North America; in Greenland a separate race occurs. Without doubt this is the commonest duck in north-west Europe. The estimates of breeding numbers which have been made in several countries suggest that at least 1,500,000 pairs nest in the region (Ogilvie 1976) and the true figure may be far higher. It has been estimated that 1,500,000 occur in winter in north-west Europe (Atkinson-Willes 1976). The species is certainly the most successful duck on the continent. Breeding numbers are increasing in most countries and the birds have a facility unique among ducks for living close to humans. Furthermore, wild stocks can be augmented by the release of hand-reared birds.

In Ireland Mallard breed throughout the country in a variety of wetland habitats from small ponds and streams to large lakes and estuaries. Densities vary considerably from one location to another and very little information is available to indicate the numbers nesting at particular sites. At Ballycotton, Cork, the writer estimated 120 pairs on a 33 hectare lake in 1968; at the Wexford Slobs there were at least 800 birds in July 1971 of which the vast majority were adult males (Merne 1972). These are sites of particularly high breeding density; over most of the country Mallard are much more thinly though widely dispersed. Sharrock (1976) has speculated that there might be an average of 20 pairs per 10-km square of the National Grid in Britain and Ireland. On this assumption the Irish breeding population would be in the region of 20,000 pairs.

After breeding, Mallard tend to congregate in large flocks on certain lakes and estuaries. In August and September much the largest numbers appear on Lough Neagh, the Wexford Slobs, Lough Corrib, Lough Derravaragh and Lough Iron as family parties join up with non-breeders and some immigrants (Fig. 24).

At certain locations these flocks disperse in October and November, for example at the Wexford Slobs and Ballycotton where the largest numbers occur on the south coast (Fig. 24). At other locations, such as Strangford Lough, there is a less marked dispersal, and at some, such as Portumna at the north end of Lough Derg, the numbers increased in winter (Fig. 25). These fluctuations are certainly due in part to a dispersal from large waters to smaller ponds and marshes in late autumn and early

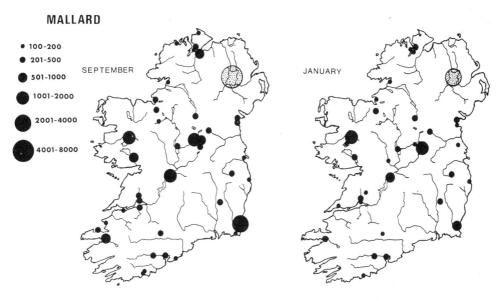

Fig. 24. Principal concentrations of Mallard in Ireland in September and January. Stippling indicates an assessment based on counts prior to 1971. All other assessments are based on the mean of the counts from 1971-72 to 1974-75.

winter. Some, however, may emigrate in late autumn and there is some slight evidence for this in the form of four hand-reared birds released in Wexford in autumn 1970 which were shot in France before the end of the following January (Merne 1971). These were probably 'abmigrants', birds which had travelled with immigrants from France as they returned to their breeding area.

Ringing recoveries show that there is some immigration in autumn, but that the immigrants form quite a small proportion of our winter population. Birds ringed as newly hatched young in England, Scotland and Iceland have been recovered in Ireland in winter; birds ringed in Ireland in autumn and winter have been recovered in Scandinavia, the Baltic states and Britain in subsequent autumns. As these birds may have already been migrating when shot we cannot be certain of their country of origin. However, the vast majority of Irish ringed Mallard have been recovered within a radius of 15 kilometres of the ringing site (B. Stronach pers. comm.). To a certain extent this is more a measure of the life expectancy of Mallard than an indication of the proportion of sedentary birds as most were shot within a few weeks of being trapped and ringed. But excluding those recovered in the same winter in which they were ringed it is still clear that a large proportion of the Mallard present in Ireland in winter are resident and sedentary birds.

Large numbers of hand-reared Mallard are now released every autumn by gun clubs with financial assistance from the Department of Fisheries (Forest and Wildlife Service) in the Republic. The numbers released under this scheme in three recent years are set out in Table 27. The table also shows the large proportion released in Wexford.

In Northern Ireland several hundred are released annually on Strangford Lough. There are no published data to indicate whether these programmes have been successful in increasing the wild population, but a policy of releasing birds in autumn on sanctuaries where they are protected for their first winter has been shown to increase breeding numbers in Britain. Research in Ireland might produce a similar result as hand-reared birds are usually well protected from shooting and often remain semi-tame.

As Mallard are widely dispersed throughout the country it is difficult to make an estimate of the mid-winter numbers. However, there are certainly more than 20,000 but probably less than 50,000 birds present in mid-January. In autumn the number is considerably larger.

Table 27

Numbers of hand-reared Mallard released in the Republic of Ireland

	Total	Wexford	Other counties
1972/73	7,984	1,395	5,589
1973/74	10,697	1,635	9,062
1974/75	10,089	1,662	8,427

Female Mallard on nest. Note the value of the plumage as camouflage.

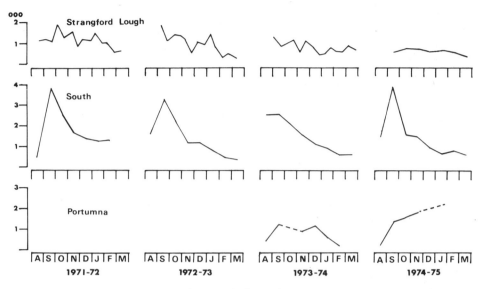

Fig. 25: Numbers of Mallard at Strangford Lough, the south coast wetlands of Wexford, Waterford and Cork and Portumna, 1971-72 to 1974-75. Counts of Portumna for the first two winters are incomplete and have been excluded.

Teal *Anas crecca*

Teal are very small and fast-flying ducks which occur, mostly in small parties, in every type of wetland habitat. The drake has a grey body, a white horizontal line along the side and yellowish under-tail-coverts. The head is brick-red with a green patch on each side, but at long range and without binoculars appears a uniform dark brown. The duck is mottled greyish-brown, rather greyer than most other Irish ducks. On the water Teal are best identified by their small size, squat bodies and small heads. In the air they look rather wader-like because of their size, fast wing-beats and preference for tight flocks.

The race which commonly occurs in Ireland, *A. c. crecca,* breeds in Iceland, northern Europe south as far as southern France and the Black Sea, and across northern Asia. In North America a separate race occurs, the Green-winged Teal, *A. c. carolinensis,* examples of which reach Ireland every winter. The drake may be separated from our bird by the absence of the white horizontal line on the side and the presence instead of a vertical white stripe on the side of the breast in front of the wing. Nobody has yet published an estimate of the number of Teal breeding in Europe. In winter Teal spread south as far as north Africa and at this season the total in north-west Europe has been estimated at 150,000 (Atkinson-Willes 1976).

In Ireland Teal are thinly distributed as breeding birds and particularly scattered south of a line from Limerick to Dundalk. During fieldwork for *The Atlas of Breeding Birds in Britain and Ireland* Teal were recorded in 386 10-km squares and proved to breed in 182. Sharrock (1976) estimated the average number per occupied 10-km square as probably three to five pairs. On this basis the Irish breeding population might be in the region of 800-1,500 pairs.

From August onwards numbers increase as immigrants arrive. On the east coast there is a reasonably steady build-up to a December peak (Fig. 26) but on the south coast many of the birds which arrive in autumn appear to move on, perhaps farther south to western France and Spain. Teal, however, react rapidly to the onset of cold weather and in mild winters, such as the four from 1971-72 to 1974-75, fewer reach Ireland than in harsh winters. The coldest weather in Britain and the Netherlands during these four years was in the last week of November 1973 and this drove many Teal west to Ireland, producing in most areas the highest counts since the 1960s in the

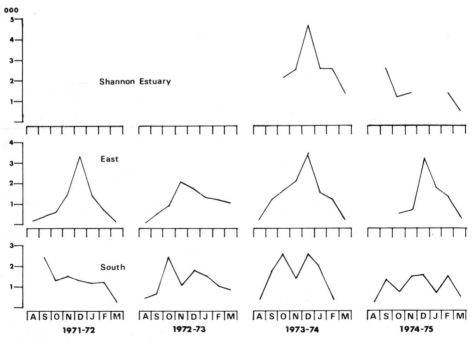

Fig. 26. Numbers of Teal at the Shannon Estuary, the east coast wetlands from the Boyne south to Broad Lough and the south coast wetlands, 1971-72 to 1974-75. Counts of the Shannon Estuary for the first two winters are incomplete and have been excluded.

following month (Fig. 26). Clearly, most of these immigrants returned shortly after the temperature rose again, for numbers in January 1974 were much reduced. In severe winters it is probable that very large numbers of Teal reach Ireland, but there have been no winters sufficiently cold to test this hypothesis since the counts began. However, recoveries of ringed birds during the extremely cold months of January, February and March 1963 indicated a massive rush of Teal to Ireland, followed by a departure of many to the coast of France and Spain as conditions remained hard. More ringed Teal were recovered in Spain in that winter than in the preceding ten winters combined (Ogilvie 1975).

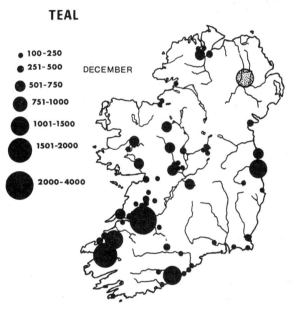

In December, when numbers are at their highest, Teal are found in small numbers throughout the country and in concentrations of several hundred on a number of wetlands (Fig. 27). The largest numbers occur on the Shannon Estuary, Tralee Bay, Castlemaine Harbour, Cork Harbour, the North Bull and the Lough Neagh basin. Ringing results show that most of these birds originate in Scandinavia and the Baltic states, though most are ringed on migration in the Netherlands (Woolf 1966). Some also come from Britain and Iceland. In January numbers decline as birds withdraw towards the breeding area. Ringing activity in the Netherlands has shown that Teal returning from

Fig. 27. Principal concentrations of Teal in Ireland in December. Conventions are as in Fig 24.

England are found there as early as the end of January but recoveries from countries to the east of the Netherlands are considerably later (Woolf 1966). However, the departure is staggered and some of the wintering Teal remain until mid-March, particularly in the Shannon valley where concentrations of over 1,000 occur on the Little Brosna until the end of the month.

The December population may be in the region of 30,000 to 50,000 birds, probably nearer the higher figure. In cold spells Ireland obviously holds many more, but until we have another harsh winter it is impossible to put a figure on the larger numbers which can occur.

The Green-winged Teal is now an annual vagrant from North America and 38 individuals were recorded in Ireland up to the end of 1976. All were adult males, the only sex which can be separated in the field from European Teal, and were recorded in the months of October (4), November (8), December (4), January (2), February (9), March (7) and April (4).

Three male and one female Teal

Gadwall *Anas strepera*

Gadwall are scarce ducks in Ireland, congregating in numbers at a very few wetlands. In shape and actions they resemble Mallard, but both sexes can be distinguished in flight by the white speculum. On the water the drake is readily separated by his slate-grey body, black 'stern' and brown head, but the duck is best identified by the flash of white speculum on the folded wing and, at close range, by the yellow bill.

These ducks breed farther south in Europe than most other species, with small populations in Ireland, Britain, Spain, France and Sweden but the majority from central Europe east across the U.S.S.R. Gadwall also breed in North America. In winter Gadwall move south to the Mediterranean and north Africa, some reaching tropical Africa. At this season there are estimated to be 10,000 in northwest Europe (Atkinson-Willes 1976).

Only a very few nest in Ireland. In the past decade breeding has been proved on Lough Neagh, in Wexford and in Kerry and cases of suspected breeding have been very few. It is most unlikely that more than about ten pairs breed in any year.

In autumn some birds arrive in September but the main immigration is in October and November. Gadwall may be seen in very small numbers, rarely more than five together, almost anywhere in the country from October to April but the main concentrations are at a very few wetlands. Largest numbers occur nowadays at Ballyallia Lake, Clare, where 180 have been counted; smaller numbers occur on Lough Neagh, Lough Carra, Lough Corrib, the south-east Wexford wetlands,

Ballycotton Lake, Cork, and several lakes in the vicinity, and Lough Gill, Kerry. Although Ruttledge (1966) referred to the Gadwall as a passage migrant and cited large concentrations in Kerry, Galway and the Shannon valley in spring and in Kerry in autumn, data collected since 1970 indicate that Gadwall are primarily winter visitors to Ireland and that passage migration, if any, is slight. The species is now very scarce in the Shannon valley at all seasons and counts at Ballyallia and Ballycotton Lakes show that the highest numbers usually occur in mid-winter. At both these sites Gadwall are sometimes scarce or even absent for short periods as the birds may move to other lakes in the vicinity. The Ballycotton birds, for example, feed and roost at other east Cork lakes when the water level is very high at the main site.

Ringing has shown that the Gadwall wintering in Ireland originate in Iceland, Scotland and Denmark. Most recoveries have been of Icelandic ringed birds, but there have been three from Loch Leven in Scotland (Allison et al 1974) and one from Denmark. The mid-winter population is somewhere in the region of 200 to 400 birds and most likely around 300 to 350. Numbers are probably increasing.

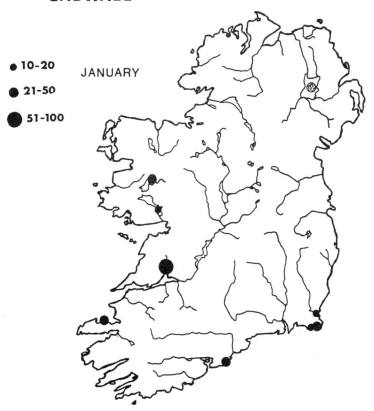

GADWALL

● 10-20   JANUARY

● 21-50

● 51-100

Fig. 28. Principal concentrations of Gadwall in Ireland in January. Conventions are as in Fig. 24.

Wigeon *Anas penelope*

Although not the best known, the Wigeon is the most numerous species of duck in Ireland during the winter. Large flocks occur on many estuaries and on the shallow lakes, turloughs and callows of the Shannon valley and the west of Ireland. Like most species of duck Wigeon have a characteristic shape. Typically, they ride quite high on the water, have short bodies, rounded heads and quite stubby bills. In flight the body looks rather dumpy, the head rounded, the neck short and the belly white in contrast to the dark breast; the adult male shows a white forewing, the female and immature male a greyish-brown forewing. On the water or on the ground, and Wigeon habitually feed by grazing, the drake is a striking bird with a rich brown head, pink breast, cream stripe from the forehead down the centre of the crown and grey back and flanks, but at long range the most obvious plumage characteristic is the white patch at the rear of the flanks contrasting with the black 'stern'. The female is best distinguished by the small size, larger than Teal but smaller than other surface-feeding ducks, rounded head, short bill and generally rufous plumage. The male's wild whistling call is utterly distinctive.

Wigeon breed in Iceland, Scotland, northern England and across northern Europe into north Asia. No estimate has been made of the number breeding in Europe, but the number breeding in Britain is considered to be only 200-300 pairs (Sharrock 1976). In autumn Wigeon move south to winter in western and south-western Europe, around the Mediterranean and Black Seas and in southern Asia (Donker 1959). This is considered to be the second most numerous surface-feeding duck in western Europe in winter, after the Mallard, with a population estimated to be between 400,000 and 500,000 birds (Atkinson-Willes 1976). Similar numbers are believed to winter around the Mediterranean.

Wigeon have been proved to nest in Ireland on only two occasions, but suspected of breeding a number of times. Single pairs nested on Lough Neagh in 1933 and on Rathlin Island, Antrim in 1953.

The first immigrants arrive usually in the last week of August and small numbers are widespread in September. In October the highest numbers are reached at Lough Foyle on the north-west coast (up to 29,000) and Castlemaine Harbour in the south-west (up to 8,000) (Fig. 30). The origin of these birds, which move on very quickly, is almost certainly Iceland. They arrive in the west of the country where one would expect birds from Iceland to first strike the coast; they arrive at about the same time as very large numbers of Whooper Swans, another common Icelandic breeding bird, appear on Lough Swilly; and there is no comparable build-up at the same time at Strangford Lough in the north-east or on the east coast estuaries where one would expect Scandinavian or Russian birds to make landfall (Fig. 30). Numbers are usually slightly reduced at Lough Foyle and Castlemaine in November, but there is a substantial increase at Strangford Lough and on the east coast, particularly at the North Bull (Hutchinson and Keys 1973). This must represent an arrival of birds from the north-east. Numbers decline at these locations in December, probably as Wigeon filter inland, but in late December and January numbers increase again in the east as colder weather drives birds west from Britain and the continent. In January Wigeon are much more widely dispersed than in November (Fig. 29).

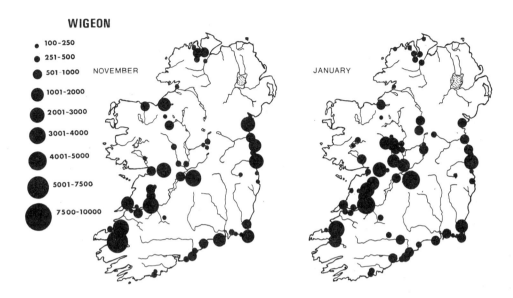

In the south and in the Shannon valley there is little indication of these autumn and mid-winter arrivals. Numbers build up much more steadily to a peak in late December or January. In February numbers decline throughout the country and this continues into March, except for an enormous spring peak in the Shannon valley (Fig. 29). This is probably accounted for by a concentration of Wigeon from the east and south in the callows on the Shannon and Little Brosna near Banagher, Offaly. But numbers are so much reduced throughout the country that it is clear there is a substantial withdrawal towards the breeding areas in February and March. Possibly the birds which congregate near Banagher are those which originate in Iceland. In April few

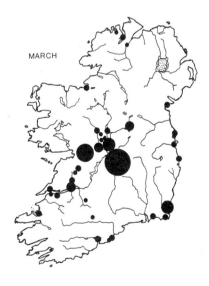

Fig. 29. Principal concentrations of Wigeon in Ireland in November, January and March. Conventions are as in Fig. 24.

remain and while occasional Wigeon spend the summer in Ireland they are very few indeed.

The movements of European Wigeon were described seventeen years ago as a result of an analysis of ringing recoveries up to 1958 (Donker 1959) and recoveries since then have confirmed the findings of that study. The Wigeon which winter in Ireland originate in Iceland, Scandinavia and Russia. Ireland is particularly important as a wintering area for Icelandic birds: 24% of the 70 recoveries abroad of birds ringed in Iceland reported up to 1958 were in Ireland. For those which breed in Scandinavia and Russia Ireland is less significant, forming the most westerly corner of a large wintering area which embraces Britain, Denmark, Belgium, the Netherlands, Germany, France and Iberia.

The peak mid-winter population was approximately 105,000 birds during the winters from 1971-72 to 1974-75. During these winters the population does not seem to have fluctuated much; there is no evidence of any marked trend towards decline or increase.

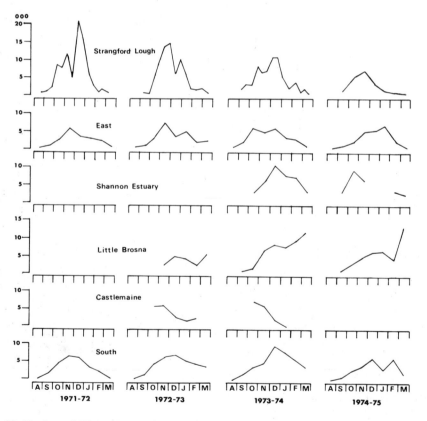

Fig. 30. Numbers of Wigeon at six sites or groups of sites, 1971-72 to 1974-75. Counts of the Shannon Estuary, the Little Brosna and Castlemaine are incomplete for some years and have been excluded.

Pintail *Anas acuta*

The Pintail is a scarce duck over most of the country. Parties of more than 25 birds occur regularly at very few locations, though smaller groups and single birds may be seen occasionally at most estuaries, marshes, shallow lakes and flooded river valleys. The drake is a beautiful bird with a long white neck, chocolate head, slender grey body and long, pointed tail. The duck is very similar to female Mallard, Gadwall and Wigeon but is slimmer, longer necked, rather greyer and more finely speckled. In flight it can be distinguished by the pale line at the rear of the wing.

Pintail are among the most numerous ducks in the world. Our birds belong to a race which breeds in northern and north-eastern Europe, across north Asia and in North America. The breeding population in Europe has been estimated at 320,000 pairs, of which 316,000 are in the Soviet Union. In mid-winter there are considered to be more than 1,300,000 in Europe, the Mediterranean basin, north-west Asia and west Africa. Very few of these, however, winter in north-west Europe which supports, according to the most recent estimate (Atkinson-Willes 1976), only 50,000 birds.

The species is an extremely rare breeding bird in Ireland. Since 1917 Pintail have nested in six counties but have never become established. During the five years of fieldwork for *The Atlas of Breeding Birds in Britain and Ireland* from 1968 to 1972 the only breeding records were of single pairs at Lough Beg, north of Lough Neagh, and in Roscommon.

As is the case throughout their entire north-west European wintering area Pintail occur in flocks at very few Irish sites (Fig. 31). The first immigrants arrive in late

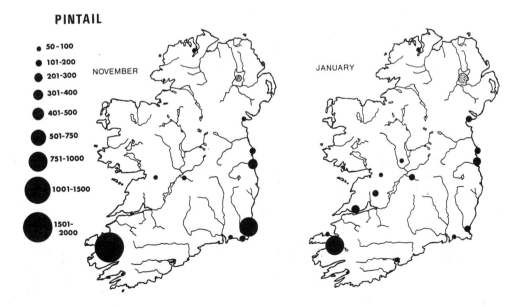

Fig. 31. Principal concentrations of Pintail in Ireland in November and January. Conventions are as in Fig. 24.

August or early September and there is a steady increase in October and November. At Castlemaine Harbour and the Wexford Slobs peak numbers are reached in this period and there is a rapid fall away from late November (Fig. 31). The Wexford birds form the great majority of those in the south shown at Fig. 32. On the east coast, largely at the North Bull and Rogerstown Estuary, the highest numbers are recorded in November or December in most years, and in three of the four years of monthly counts there was a very marked decrease in January.

Pintail show a general preference for relatively sandy estuaries and for flooded callows, but even within these broad habitat types there are many areas which are not frequented. In Britain there has been an enormous increase in the wintering population over the past decade, largely because the flock on the Mersey Estuary has increased from a peak count in 1967-68 of 1,300 to peak numbers in 1973-74 of 14,800 (Prater 1974a, 1976a). There is some evidence of a long-term increase in Ireland (Ruttledge 1966) but the only haunts for which counts are available over a prolonged period are the North Bull, Rogerstown and Strangford Lough. At the North Bull there was an increase prior to 1950 and another from 1966-67; at Rogerstown there was an increase from 1968-69; at Strangford Lough there was an increase from 1967-68. The

Two male and one female Pintail

increases, though involving relatively few birds, have been over the same period as the build-up at the Mersey just across the Irish Sea.

Ringing results indicate that some Irish Pintail come from Iceland, but that many others come from the continent, probably mostly originating in the Soviet Union. The wintering population fluctuates considerably but is probably usually between 3,000 and 7,000 birds. Peak numbers in November are probably close to the latter figure.

Shoveler *Anas clypeata*

Shoveler are widely distributed over most of the country, but concentrations of more than 50 are few. Both sexes are easily identified by the enormous spatulate bill used in sifting small organisms from the water. In flight they show a pale blue forewing and their wing-beats appear slower and heavier than those of other species. On the water they sit low, seeming to 'lurk' with the bill pointed downwards. The drake appears black and white with chestnut flanks; the head is greenish-black and the breast white. The duck resembles the female Mallard in coloration, but is somewhat richer and the spoon-like bill is very obvious.

Like Pintail these birds are extremely numerous in the western Palaearctic but only a very small proportion winter in north-west Europe. Shoveler nest in the forest zone of northern Europe from the Baltic eastwards and across Asia to Mongolia. They are also numerous in North America. The north-west European wintering population is estimated at only 20,000.

Very few nest in Ireland. During the years from 1968 to 1972 Shoveler were proved to nest in only 19 10-km squares of the National Grid and were recorded or considered likely to be nesting in another 31 squares. Most of these records were in north-east Ireland, particularly around Lough Neagh, and in Roscommon. The total breeding population is probably in the region of 100 pairs.

Shoveler are more widely distributed in Ireland in winter than Pintail. The maps at Fig. 33 do not illustrate the regular occurrence of parties of up to 20 at wetlands throughout the country. In Galway, in particular, Shoveler are much more widespread than Pintail. The first autumn birds gather early, a few appearing on estuaries in late July. These are probably Irish or British bred birds gathering to moult prior to departure for France or Iberia. In October and November an increase is noted at most locations as immigrants arrive. The largest concentration in the country is at Lough Owel, Westmeath, where up to 2,000 occur in October and November (Fig. 32). Numbers decline in December and January, and usually none remain into spring. Where these birds go is a mystery. Perhaps they disperse westwards to the Connacht turloughs or the Shannon valley. Alternatively, they may move south-west towards France or Spain.

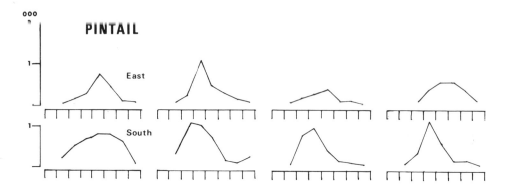

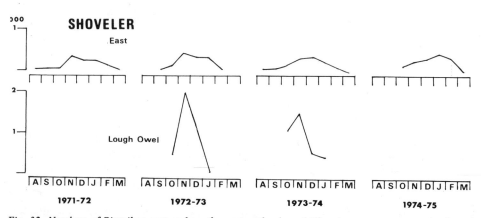

Fig. 32. Numbers of Pintail at east and south coast wetlands and Shoveler at east coast wetlands and Lough Owel, 1971-72 to 1974-75. Counts of Lough Owel for 1971-72 and 1974-75 are incomplete and have been excluded.

There is some evidence of an increase in spring. At Rahasane, Galway, and the Little Brosna the largest numbers are seen in February and March. In 1975 there was an unusually high count of 1,500 at Lough Iron, Westmeath in late February. We know that Icelandic Black-tailed Godwits assemble in the Shannon valley and Rahasane in spring and we suspect that Icelandic Wigeon do so also. Hence, the most likely explanation of the increase in Shoveler numbers in the same area is that these too are Icelandic breeding birds. However, at this time of year Shoveler have disappeared from the coastal estuaries so these birds are not necessarily returning from southern Europe, but may well have spent the winter elsewhere in Ireland.

From ringing recoveries we know that Icelandic, Scandinavian and Russian Shoveler winter in Ireland as well as some Scottish birds. The winter population is very difficult to assess, but it is likely that in November there are close to 8,000 birds in the country. By January there may be as few as 4,000 remaining.

SHOVELER

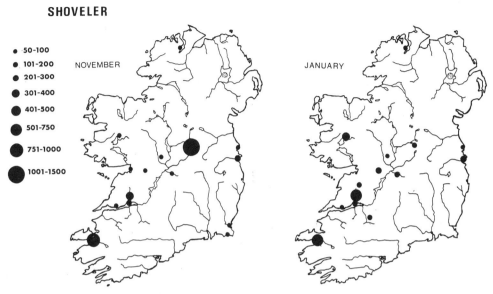

- • 50-100
- • 101-200
- ● 201-300
- ● 301-400
- ● 401-500
- ● 501-750
- ● 751-1000
- ● 1001-1500

NOVEMBER

JANUARY

Fig. 33. Principal concentrations of Shoveler in Ireland in November and January.
Conventions are as in Fig. 24.

Tufted Duck *Aythya fuligula*

Tufted Duck are common and well-known diving ducks on most of the lakes of Ireland. The adult male is easily identified by his black and white appearance. The head, breast and upperparts generally are black, contrasting with pure white flanks. At close range the thin, drooping crest on the crown which gives the bird its English name and the bright yellow eye may be seen. The adult female and immature are dark brown with sometimes a trace of whitish at the base of the bill and at close range a very short crest may be seen. In flight both sexes show a long, white wing-bar.

The breeding range of the Tufted Duck in Eurasia is very similar to that of the Wigeon and Pintail except that it breeds commonly as far west as Ireland and does not extend so far north as Siberia. In several countries estimates have been made of breeding numbers. At least 5,000 pairs nest at Lake Myvatyn in Iceland and several hundred elsewhere in that country; in Finland there are considered to be 40,000 pairs and in the Baltic states 3,500 to 4,000 pairs (Ogilvie 1975). The number wintering in north-west Europe is estimated at 500,000, at least half of which are concentrated off the Danish coast on the shallow waters of the western Baltic (Atkinson-Willes 1976). Elsewhere in northern Europe Tufted Duck occur chiefly on freshwater habitat; in Ireland they are very scarce on marine or estuarine habitat.

The Irish breeding population has been estimated at 2,000 pairs, as compared with a breeding population in Britain of 4,000-5,000 pairs (Sharrock 1976). Breeding was first proved in 1877 and the species has been increasing and extending its range ever since. The majority nest north and west of a line from Limerick to Dundalk where the majority of suitable lakes — lakes of an area of at least one hectare — are situated. The largest concentrations are of 800-1,000 pairs in the Lough Neagh basin and 200 pairs on Lower Lough Erne.

Any assessment of the Irish wintering population is complicated by the lack of recent data on the numbers occurring in the Lough Neagh basin. However, the results obtained from the counts organised by the Northern Ireland Ornithologists' Club in the late 1960s (Table 28) show that the area had the largest concentrations in northern Europe outside the western Baltic and the Ijsselmeer in Holland. Elsewhere in Ireland there are late autumn and mid-winter concentrations of over 500 on the Westmeath lakes, Lough Ree, the Lough Erne system and in Wexford. Smaller concentrations occur on most of the large lakes and parties of ten or so may be met with almost anywhere. A review of the distribution in November and January (Fig. 34) shows no

Adult male Tufted Duck

TUFTED DUCK

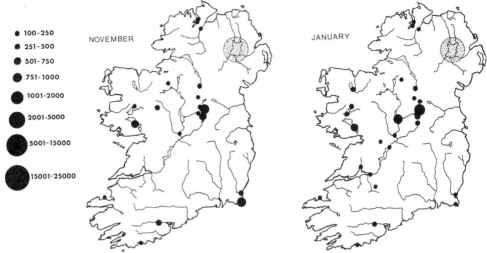

Fig. 34. Principa, concentrations of Tufted Duck in Ireland in November and January.
Conventions are as in Fig. 24.

significant difference between the two months. The one apparent difference — the lack of registration of any concentration at Lough Ree in November — arises because of the lack of data rather than because we know that none was present.

We know very little about the movements of Irish bred Tufted Duck after the breeding season, but some at least winter in the country. In late July large numbers (up to several thousand) have been reported from Lough Cullin, Mayo, presumably a

Table 28

Numbers of Tufted Duck at the Lough Neagh basin, 1964-65 to 1968-69. The absence of figures indicates that no counts were made in those months.

Month	1964-65	1965-66	1966-67	1967-68	1968-69
August			3,697	5,294	3,412
September			9,303	7,358	8,547
October		25,823	18,451	11,645	25,746
November		20,879	14,967	28,856	16,977
December		30,445	17,632		
January	17,978	21,693	15,653		34,176
February	17,154	14,500	12,246	27,859	
March	11,817	11,911	10,626	12,242	
April		5,204	5,052	4,279	
May		1,802	2,287	2,036	

moulting flock. These disperse during the autumn. The main influx of immigrants at the Westmeath lakes and Lough Neagh appears to be in late September or October and the departure from the arrival back at the closely studied Scottish colony at Loch Leven (Allison et al 1974). Most of these Scottish birds winter in Ireland. Some of the Loch Levin birds arrive in autumn and the great bulk of them are present from December to February. Other immigrants visit us from Iceland and some also from Scandinavia and the Baltic countries.

Because Tufted Duck are so widely dispersed in small numbers the mid-winter population is very difficult to estimate. The best assessment at present would be of a population somewhere between 10,000 and 25,000 birds, excluding altogether those at Lough Neagh. In Britain the wintering population doubled between 1954 and 1965, but appears to have stabilised since (Ogilvie 1975). We do not know if a similar increase occurred in Ireland.

Pochard *Aythya ferina*

Pochard are not quite so well known as Tufted Duck, probably because the plumage is not so striking, but they are almost as widely distributed. The male has a chestnut head, pale grey back and flanks and black breast and 'stern'. The female is dull brown and grey with paleness about the base of the bill, cheeks and throat. It is paler than the Tufted Duck and both sexes have a more hump-backed appearance than that species. In flight Pochard show a grey wing-bar where the Tufted Duck shows a white stripe.

Pochard breed from eastern Britain across central Europe and Asia, but keeping farther south than most Tufted Duck. They do not breed in Iceland. In winter they move south, mostly around the Mediterranean and Black Sea, but 250,000 are estimated to winter in north-west Europe (Atkinson-Willes 1974).

In Ireland the Pochard is a rare breeder. Though nesting was first recorded as long ago as 1907 the species has not been nearly as successful as the Tufted Duck in extending its range. It now nests only sporadically and in very small numbers, mainly in the midlands. The total breeding in any one year might be as few as ten pairs.

We do not know when most Pochard arrive in Ireland in autumn, but enormous numbers are present at Lough Corrib and Lough Derravaragh in September, the earliest month for which we have complete counts. However, counts at the south-east corner of Lough Corrib in early autumn 1975 showed that a flock was present as early as 17th July, the great majority of which were males. Although not indicated in Fig. 35, Lough Cullin in Mayo is believed to be another haunt where substantial numbers of Pochard occur in autumn, though winter counts have shown quite low numbers. In late July 1975 a flock of approximately 4,000 diving duck was seen on this lake. It included both Tufted Duck and Pochard. These three lakes are almost certainly used by moulting Pochard; similar flocks are known to occur at certain other European lakes (Salomonsen 1968). In view of the predominance of males at Lough Corrib in July 1975 it is interesting that in Bavaria and the Netherlands males arrive at these large assemblies in June and July, the females (less than 10% of the numbers) not until August.

The flocks at these three lakes disperse from October onwards and Pochard appear in some numbers at other wetlands (Fig. 35). Although quite widely dispersed in winter there are some marked differences from the pattern of distribution of the Tufted Duck

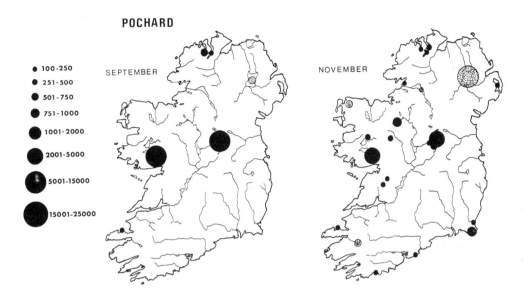

POCHARD

(Fig. 34). Pochard do not occur in large numbers on the Shannon lakes or the Lee reservoirs in Cork. Tufted Duck do not occur in such numbers on the north Clare and south Galway lakes. The main reason for this is probably the difference in the diet: Pochard are largely vegetarian, feeding on water plants and seeds; Tufted Duck are animal feeders, preferring small molluscs, crustaceans and insect larvae.

The counts at Lough Neagh in the late 1960s showed that this was the second most common species of duck after the Tufted Duck (Table 29). While numbers fluctuated greatly from year to year the highest count was always in the period from November to February. Data from other Irish

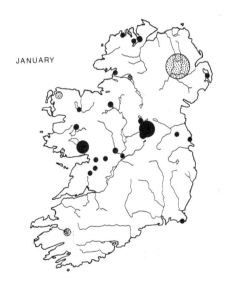

Fig. 35. *Principal concentratiins of Pochard in Ireland in September, November and January. Conventions are as in Fig. 24.*

wetlands show that most Pochard leave between mid-February and mid March. We do not yet know where Ireland's wintering population breeds; most of the very few ringed birds recovered in Ireland were ringed on passage in England. But some birds ringed in Ireland in recent years have been recovered quite far east in Russia in summer (O. J. Merne, pers. comm.).

The winter population is as difficult to estimate as that of the Tufted Duck but it seems likely to be somewhere between 15,000 and 35,000 birds.

Table 29

Numbers of Pochard at the Lough Neagh basin, 1964-65 to 1968-69. The absence of figures indicates that no counts were made in those months.

Month	1964-65	1965-66	1966-67	1967-68	1968-69
August			80	72	505
September			29	579	534
October		2,552	2,916	3,375	3,874
November		16,450	3,855	11,710	8,126
December		28,161	11,265		
January	6,924	37,648	6,895		14,485
February	14,185	5,507	3,214	7,312	
March	4,948	1,442	744	294	
April	49	—	—	48	
May	6	2	2	10	

Goldeneye *Bucephala clangula*

The Goldeneye is a much less common diving duck than the Tufted Duck or Pochard. The adult male, which is much scarcer than the adult female or immature, is a striking bird with a black head and small white spot near the base of the bill. The back is black with a white patch and the breast, flanks and underparts generally are white. The adult female and immature have a chocolate head, separated from a greyish body by a white collar, more noticeable in the adult female than the immature. But the best identification features are the large and peaked head and the carriage of the body low in the water, tapering to the waterline at the tail. At long range or in poor light these features are diagnostic.

Goldeneye breed in the forest zone from Scandinavia east across the northern U.S.S.R. Another race breeds in North America. Although breeding has been proved in Scotland in recent years it has never been suspected in Ireland. The north-west European winter population is estimated at 150,000 of which two-thirds are in the Baltic and perhaps 10,000-12,000 in Britain and Ireland (Szijj 1972).

As with the Tufted Duck and Pochard any assessment of the status of the species is hampered by the lack of recent data on Lough Neagh. The counts in the late 1960s (Table 30) showed numbers which fluctuated considerably from year to year with up to 5,400 counted. Elsewhere in Ireland the first birds are usually seen in October and the main arrival is in late October and early November. Although there were a few at

Party of eight Pochard

Table 30

Numbers of Goldeneye at the Lough Neagh basin, 1964-65 to 1968-69. The absence of figures indicates that no counts were made in those months

Month	1964-65	1965-66	1966-67	1967-68	1968-69
August			20	30	9
September			25	87	17
October		799	748	209	890
November		4,756	4,233	1,709	2,251
December		6,134	2,355		
January	3,466	3,431	3,275		3,224
February	3,513	4,138	3,661	5,925	
March	4,725	4,765	5,722	4,802	
April		586	1,894	670	
May		68	102	13	

Lough Neagh in August and September the main arrival there was clearly at the same time. The peak counts at other Irish sites were made in various months but there is a tendency for larger numbers in January and February. Numbers tend to decline in March and few remain into April. However, since the population in the rest of the country is less than 2,000 birds, probably between 1,000 and 1,800, the Lough Neagh numbers are clearly so significant that it is impossible to draw general conclusions on the trend in numbers between 1971-72 and 1974-75 because of the absence of data.

Results from ringing in Sweden show that many Irish wintering Goldeneye breed in northern Sweden (Nilsson 1969).

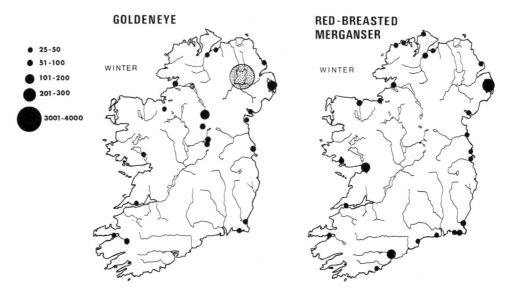

Fig. 36. Principal concentrations of Goldeneye and Red-breasted Mergansers in Ireland in winter. Conventions are as in Fig. 24.

Red-breasted Merganser *Mergus serrator*

Red-breasted Mergansers are common and relatively familiar coastal, diving, 'saw-billed' ducks. They are slim, slender-necked birds which show quite prominent crests. The male has a dark green head separated from a chestnut breast by a white collar. The back and tail are black and the flanks grey. The female is drabber with a brown head merging into a browngh-grey neck and upperparts generally. Both sexes have long, fine bills and a broad white speculum in flight.

The species is a northerly breeder, nesting from Ireland and Iceland north-east across Scandinavia, around the Baltic and the northern U.S.S.R. into northern Asia. It also breeds in North America. Winter counts suggest a north-west European population of 40,000 birds (Szijj 1972) of which 5,000-10,000 are in Britain and Ireland (Ogilvie 1975).

Although in winter the Red-breasted Merganser occurs chiefly on the coast it breeds well inland in Ireland. The breeding population is quite thinly distributed north and west of a line from west Cork to north Louth. The only regular breeding birds east of this line are in south-east Wexford. An estimate based on three to five pairs per 10-km square of confirmed or probable breeding during 1968-72, as suggested by Sharrock (1976), would total about 500-850 pairs.

In autumn there are indications that a flock assembles off the north Dublin coast to moult. Counts of 400-450 in July 1967 and 300 in late August 1970 (Ruttledge 1975) have been recorded. There have also been records of large flocks in early August in Dundrum Bay, Down. But while birds move about the coast there is no evidence of any large scale immigration in winter. Numbers remain relatively constant from September to March. However, the size of the mid-winter population, probably between 2,000 and 3,000 birds, implies some immigration in autumn to augment the relatively small post-breeding population. One Icelandic ringed bird has been recovered in Mayo, but no Scandinavian birds have been found here.

The largest winter numbers are found in Strangford Lough, Cork Harbour and Galway Bay (Fig. 36). Smaller numbers are found in other estuaries and parties of up to 25 may be met with almost anywhere along the coast. The lack of records from west Galway and Mayo almost certainly reflects the absence of observations rather than a paucity of birds.

Shelduck *Tadorna tadorna*

Although restricted to the coast and in large numbers to a very few estuaries the Shelduck is a well known bird, probably because of its large size and striking plumage. In general appearance the Shelduck is rather goose-like. The neck is long, the forehead steep and the stance much more upright than other duck. The plumage of both sexes is similar. The head is very dark green, appearing black at a distance, and the body generally white with a chestnut band across the lower breast, black stripes along each wing and a red bill.

In north-west Europe the Shelduck is an exclusively coastal breeder, but from the Caspian east across the southern U.S.S.R. and into China it breeds inland, frequently hundreds, even thousands, of kilometres from the sea. The species is easy to count because of its large size and obvious coloration. In north-west Europe the assembly of at least 90% of the population off Heligoland for the post-breeding moult provides further opportunities for assessing the numbers in this area. Aerial surveys at the moulting grounds in the 1960s gave totals of 80,000-90,000 birds, showing close correlation with the January 1969 census total for north-west Europe of 95,000 (Ogilvie 1975).

Shelduck breed around most of the coast of Ireland, at Lough Neagh, Lower Lough Erne and Poulaphouca Reservoir, Wicklow. There are gaps in the breeding distribution in north Mayo, west Clare, south Kerry and north Wexford, sections of the coastline which have very few muddy areas. Research has shown that territories are established in muddy areas where the main food, the mollusc *Hydrobia ulvae,* is found (Young 1970, Jenkins *et al* 1975).

Shelduck do not nest until they are two years old so a number of non-breeders are present in summer. In July most of those which have nested leave their ducklings in

Shelduck in flight

creches in the care of a few adults and, together with the non-breeders, move to the Heligoland Bight to moult. Some may go to Bridgwater Bay, Somerset in England where *c.* 3,000 Shelduck moult, arriving after the local adults have left (Eltringham and Boyd 1963), but more ringing of Irish Shelduck is required if a connection is to be proven. There are already two recoveries of German ringed Shelducks in Ireland to prove that some at least moult near Heligoland.

The timing of the return from the moult varies from year to year, but the first birds usually arrive in mid-October and there is a steady build-up until January. The peak counts at most estuaries are in the months from January to March: at the North Bull the peak is in January, at Strangford Lough and the Shannon Estuary in February or March, at Cork Harbour in March. The larger numbers on certain estuaries in early spring may be British birds which have wandered westwards. There is little evidence of immigration from other countries. One Norwegian ringed bird was recovered in Ireland in its first winter, but one would expect more recoveries both in Ireland and Britain if many foreign birds wintered in these islands.

The numbers wintering in Ireland are somewhere between 6,500 and 8,500 birds. Although there has been a considerable increase in the British Shelduck population over the past ten years this has not been reflected in Ireland. In fact, there is evidence of a decline since the late 1960s. Certainly, numbers at Cork Harbour have never since approached the 2,400 counted in March 1968, nor has the Rogerstown wintering flock

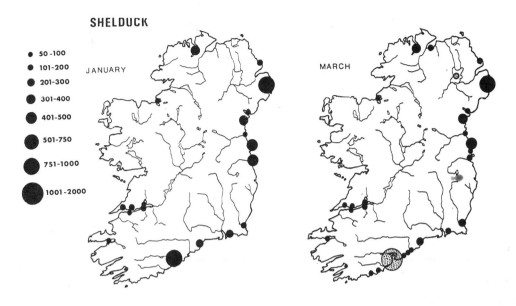

Fig. 37. *Principal concentrations of Shelduck in Ireland in January and March.*
Conventions are as in Fig. 24.

reached anything like the 1,000 which wintered in 1968-69. Unfortunately, there are very few counts available for the 1960s and a detailed comparison is impossible for most other estuaries. During the winters from 1971-72 to 1974-75 there was no indication of any marked change in status.

Sea Ducks

In addition to the species already discussed four species of duck occur reasonably commonly in Ireland but are not typically wetland species. The Scaup *Aythya marila,* Long-tailed Duck *Clangula hyemalis,* Common Scoter *Melanitta nigra* and Eider *Somateria mollissima* are sea ducks, much more marine than the other species we have been considering. While they may be found in estuaries, and Scaup may even be found inland on Lough Neagh, they are more frequently found in bays along the coast. However, for the sake of completeness a brief account of their status, drawn from various sources, is given here.

Scaup are mainly winter visitors to Ireland, though Ruttledge (1970) has written that numbers are higher in autumn and spring, indicating some passage migration. During this survey monthly counts were carried out at Carlingford Lough and no evidence of autumn or spring passage was noted. However, the status has changed in recent years. Prior to 1966 several hundred wintered off the Meath coast and *c.* 3,000 in Wexford Harbour. None now occur off Meath and very small numbers in Wexford

Harbour. The current status, based on data from this survey and Ruttledge (1970), is shown at Fig. 38.

The Long-tailed Duck is much the scarcest of these sea ducks. Only in Greatman's Bay, Galway and off Portnoo, Donegal are more than ten found regularly and there the numbers are rarely over 25. Smaller numbers are found in Dublin Bay, along the Cork coast, in Clew Bay, Mayo, Trawbreaga Bay, Donegal, Belfast Lough and Dundrum Bay, Down. Larger numbers are occasionally seen in April.

The Common Scoter (Fig. 38), like the Scaup, is now less abundant in winter than formerly. Up to 1963 much larger numbers were found on the east coast. There is evidence of passage migration at Cape Clear, Cork from mid-June to August (Sharrock 1973) and some birds remain throughout the summer off the coast, particularly in Kerry. Unlike the last two species Common Scoters nest in Ireland Over 100 pairs nest at Lough Erne and 20-30 pairs at Lough Conn, the only two breeding sites (Ferguson 1968, 1971).

We know very little about the Irish Eider population. The species breeds from north Down round the north coast to Inishmurray, Sligo, having colonised Ireland in 1912. There is no evidence of any very recent spread. In winter Eiders are rare birds anywhere south of the breeding range and it seems that the Irish breeders are extremely sedentary.

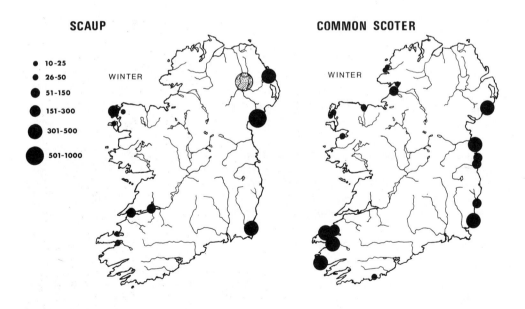

Fig. 38. Principal concentrations of Scaup and Common Scoter in Ireland in winter. Conventions are as in Fig. 24.

Rare Ducks

A further 15 species of duck have been recorded infrequently in Ireland. Six of these are North American species which occur as vagrants on this side of the Atlantic. The Black Duck *Anas rubripes,* a species closely allied to the Mallard, has been recorded on only three occasions, but the Blue-winged Teal *Anas discors* has been recorded 22 times and the American Wigeon *Anas americana* 11 times up to the end of 1976. A remarkable record was the occurrence of 13 American Wigeon at Akeragh Lough, Kerry in October 1968. One which was shot was found to have been ringed in Canada in August, two months earlier. At least four Ring-necked Ducks *Aythya collaris* have been recorded up to the end of 1976. One was present at Lurgan Park Lake, Armagh, also visiting Lough Neagh, each winter from 1959-60 to 1969-70, two being present from 1965-66 to 1968-69. The species resembles the Tufted Duck and occurred in Armagh with Tufted Ducks. The Surf Scoter *Melanitta perspicillata* has been recorded 11 times in winter and the Hooded Merganser *Mergus cucullatus* on three occasions. The Surf Scoter is tending to occur more frequently, but the only record of a Hooded Merganser this century was in 1957.

Eight of the remaining nine species are European. The Garganey *Anas querquedula* is a small duck about the size of a Teal and is recorded annually on spring and autumn passage. This is the only duck species occurring in Ireland which winters almost exclusively in Africa, returning north to Europe to breed. Breeding has been proved in Ireland on only two occasions but suspected a number of times at Lough Neagh. The Red-crested Pochard *Netta rufina* and Ferruginous Duck *Aythya nyroca* have been recorded 14 and 13 times respectively. Unlike the American vagrants, which are being reported with increasing regularity, these two species are still extremely rare. The Velvet Scoter *Melanitta fusca* is an annual autumn and winter visitor, mainly to the east coast where up to 40 have been recorded in November. The King Eider *Somateria spectabilis* has been recorded seven or eight times. The Goosander *Mergus merganser,* a larger relative of the Red-breasted Merganser, is a scarce but annual winter visitor, chiefly to inland waters. While birds are usually seen singly small parties are sometimes recorded. A pair bred in the north of the country in at least four of the years from 1969 to 1975. The Smew *Mergus albellus,* a much smaller 'saw-billed' duck, is rarer but occurs in winter in most years, almost always singly. The Ruddy Shelduck *Tadorna ferruginea* is a very rare vagrant from Europe, last recorded in 1955. The last species of duck recorded in Ireland is the Baikal Teal *Anas formosa,* a beautiful Asian duck. One was shot in Fermanagh in January 1967, but it has been suggested that the bird might have escaped from a wildfowl collection.

Fuller details of the status of these rarer species are available to the interested reader in the standard works on Irish birds (Ruttledge 1966 and 1975) and in the annual 'Irish Bird Report', published in the journal *Irish Birds*.

GEESE AND SWANS

The geese and the swans are two groups of wildfowl which have little in common other than being much larger than the ducks, the other main group of wildfowl. Geese are large-bodied grazing birds which rarely feed while swimming on the water. Most feed on rough pasture land or indeed on agricultural crops though Brent Geese feed on the seashore. They all resemble the farmyard goose to some extent and have rather rotund bodies, long and straight necks and much stouter bills than ducks. When on land they have a very erect stance; on the water they appear very bulky and hold the tail cocked. Geese fall into two groups: the 'grey' and the 'black' geese. Six species of grey goose and three of black have been recorded in Ireland, though only two of each could be considered common.

Swans are even larger than geese and their shape and colour are completely different. Swans have larger and longer bodies, much longer necks, proportionately shorter legs and longer bills. The adults of the species which occur in Ireland are all white and the juveniles dingy greyish-brown. They feed by upending or plucking food from the surface of the water; they graze, but less frequently than geese. In any event a flock of grazing swans is more likely to be mistaken for sheep than geese.

Geese occur in Ireland in large numbers at relatively few sites and censuses had been made of all the common species prior to the commencement of the *Wetlands Enquiry*. Indeed, the species accounts which follow owe more to the published data on special studies of the birds than to counts made for the *Enquiry*. Swans have been less well studied, though a breeding census of Mute Swans was attempted in 1976 and a winter census of Bewick's Swans in 1975-76.

Ireland is an extremely important wintering area for Greenland White-fronted Geese, Greenland and Canadian Brent Geese, Whooper Swans and Bewick's Swans. About 70% of the world population of the Greenland race of the White-fronted Goose winters in Ireland and most of these occur at the Wexford Slobs. Their conservation is a matter for which Ireland has a unique responsibility. Almost all the European wintering birds of the Greenland and Canadian populations of the Brent Goose winter in Ireland and their conservation is also, in a European context, a strictly Irish responsibility. However, the situation is not as critical as with the White-fronted Goose for this population of Brent Goose also winters in eastern North America. The world population of the Whooper Swan is not fully known, but Ireland's 4,000-6,000 birds are a high proportion. As many Irish birds are known to come from Iceland it is probable that, as with several other waterfowl species, the bulk of the Icelandic breeding population winters here. In the case of the Bewick's Swan Ireland's conservation responsibility is similar to that for the White-fronted Goose. The Bewick's Swan is a much scarcer bird in Europe than the Greenland White-fronted Goose and Ireland holds some 22% of the population. Conservationists have not yet faced up to the need to take positive measures to ensure the protection of sufficient habitat for this swan in Ireland.

Greenland Whitefronted Geese and Bewick's Swans on the North Slob, Co. Wexford.

Greylag Goose *Anser anser*

The Greylag is the largest of our regularly wintering geese. As its name implies, it is a grey goose, closely resembling the farmyard goose. Its plumage is generally grey with white under tail coverts. Its head is large and the bird's body looks very bulky, but one of the best characteristics for identification is the very pale grey forewing obvious in flight. The bill is bright orange.

The nominate race, which concerns us here, breeds in Iceland and from northern Scandinavia south to Denmark and Greece. Another race, with a pink bill, breeds from south-west Europe to Siberia.

The Irish wintering population is now very small and restricted to eight locations (Fig. 39). The total number of birds involved is probably between 750 and 1,000, but there are fluctuations from year to year at some sites. In January 1967 a total of 740 was counted in the only census carried out so far (Cabot 1967a). Birds arrive in mid-October and depart about the end of March. In autumn, during the period from mid-October to mid-November, single birds and small parties may be seen almost anywhere on the coast and even at some inland wetlands.

There has been a marked change in status this century. On the Wexford Slobs the population was estimated at 6,000-10,000 birds annually up to 1945-46 when a rapid decline began. By 1956 there were less than 220 wintering in the entire area (Ruttledge and Hall Watt 1958) and in the 1960s these dwindled away. Nowadays it is exceptional for more than a handful of Greylag Geese to be seen on the Wexford Slobs. During the period of the decline in Ireland there was a corresponding increase in Scotland.

This is probably the species of goose which bred in the Bog of Allen and in Co. Down in the eighteenth century (Ussher and Warren 1900). Nowadays there is a small feral population at Strangford Lough.

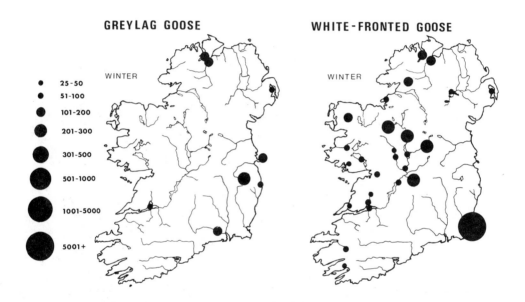

Fig. 39. Principal concentrations of Greylag Geese and White-fronted Geese in Ireland in winter. Conventions are as in Fig 24.

White-fronted Goose *Anser albifrons*

The White-fronted Goose is the most widespread Irish grey goose. It is smaller and browner than the Greylag and the body is more angular in shape. The adult has a white forehead and black bars on the underparts, though some immatures show a white forehead, especially late in the winter.

The race which winters commonly in Ireland, *A. a. flavirostris,* breeds in western Greenland and winters only in Ireland, western Scotland and, in very small numbers, in Wales. The total population is probably in the region of 12,000-15,000 birds. The nominate race breeds in north-east Russia, Siberia and North America, wintering in Europe as far south as France. Two other races occur in North America. The Greenland breeding birds have an orange-yellow bill. Those which breed in Europe have a shorter pink bill and are slightly paler and greyer in plumage.

White-fronted Geese winter in large numbers on the Wexford Slobs, where 5,000-7,000 birds occur, and in smaller scattered flocks on bogs, callows, islands and pasture fields near water throughout the midlands and west of Ireland. These geese are scarce in Munster. Arrival is generally from the end of September and departure is in April and early May.

The size of the Irish population is difficult to estimate because the birds are so scattered, but a census in 1967, partly based on an aerial survey, produced 8,243 birds (Cabot 1967c) and this census omitted such important areas as the Bog of Erris and the bogs of Connemara. Numbers fluctuate, however, from year to year, the main reason being variation in breeding success in Greenland. As Table 31 clearly shows, larger numbers occurred at the Wexford Slobs following summers with a reasonably high rate of breeding success. There is evidence of a decline throughout the midlands and west of Ireland over the past twenty years, but the causes are not known. There appears to have been no similar decrease on the Wexford Slobs and at Islay in Scotland there has been a significant increase, possibly corresponding to the Irish decrease, from c. 2,500 in the 1950s to 3,500-4,000 in the 1970s.

The earlier history of the White-fronted Goose in Ireland is not well known, though

Greenland White-fronted Geese on the Wexford Slobs.

Portrait of an adult Greenland White-fronted Goose

we do know that the species was much scarcer on the Slobs than the Greylag Goose up to 1925 (Kennedy *et al* 1954). There was a considerable increase after 1935.

The European White-fronted Goose *A. a. albifrons* is a rare winter visitor. Up to eight occur in most winters on the Wexford Slobs.

Table 31

Peak winter counts of White-fronted Geese at the Wexford Slobs, 1968-69 to 1976-77, and annual percentage of juveniles.

Winter	Peak count	Percentage juveniles
1968-69	6,244	35%
1969-70	7,000	35%
1970-71	7,000	14%
1971-72	5,958	12%
1972-73	5,565	12%
1973-74	5,296	15%
1974-75	5,800	18%
1975-76	6,019	21%
1976-77	6,700	20%

Brent Goose *Branta bernicla*

The Brent is the smallest and darkest Irish goose, about the same size as a Shelduck. The head, neck and breast are black with a whitish patch on each side of the neck; the mantle, back and wings are ash-grey, the belly is pale greyish and the under-tail-coverts are brilliant white. This is exclusively a coastal species, feeding mainly on eel grass *Zostera* and algae on estuaries.

Although there were long considered to be three races of the Brent Goose recent examination of birds on the Canadian Arctic breeding grounds has shown such a range of plumage variation even within a small population

that it is safest to treat the Brent as one species with several populations but without readily separable subspecies. Brent Geese breed in Svalbard (Spitzbergen), Greenland, Arctic Canada, Siberia and Russia and winter in Europe as far south as France. The Irish wintering population breeds in Arctic Canada and presumably in Greenland.

The Irish population has been censused on a number of occasions since 1960-61. The results of these censuses are set out in the adjoining table. In 1950 there were an estimated 6,000 in Ireland (Ruttledge 1975). Numbers have increased considerably, though there was a decrease in the mid-1960s, probably following poor breeding seasons. Nowadays there are probably more Brent wintering in Ireland than ever before: the species is now much the most numerous goose in Ireland.

As the map indicates (Fig. 40), the main arrival in autumn is concentrated at Strangford Lough and the north-west Kerry bays. In most years very large flocks also occur at Sligo Bay, but only for a short period in October. Passage is also noticed at Lough Foyle in some years. Arrival is earliest in Kerry where the first birds are present in late August. The main arrival, however, is in October.

During the winter the large concentration at Strangford Lough disperses, many birds moving south to the Dublin and Wexford estuaries. Colour-marking of Brent Geese in the Canadian High Arctic by means of a large numbered band on the neck has shown that many of our birds nest on the Queen Elizabeth Islands in northern Canada (Maltby-Prevett *et al* 1975). Birds from the same breeding area also winter on the Atlantic coast of North America.

Since the increase in the early 1970s Brent have shown a tendency to feed on pasture fields, winter wheat and even seed grain in Co. Wexford, on stubble fields in Co. Donegal and on a golf-course in Co. Dublin.

Table 32

Results of censuses of Irish wintering Brent Geese and percentage of juveniles where known.

Winter	November	CENSUS TOTAL January	February	% Juveniles
1960-61	11,909	10,952		
1961-62	12,052			
1965-66	7,348		5,513	2% (n=1,459)
1966-67	8,058		6,208	16% (n=804)
1967-68	8,314		7,540	6% (n=966)
1968-69	7,765			
1969-70				47% (n=531)
1970-71	12,000			good
1971-72				26% approx (n. unknown)
1972-73	11,168			2% (n=507)
1973-74	16,140			v. good
1974-75	11,600			0% (n=1,000 approx.)
1975-76				40% (n=695)
1977-78		9,300		19% (n=3,026)

Note: the loss of birds between the earlier and later counts in years when two counts were made is probably due to a combination of mortality and birds being missed after dispersal from the main haunts.

Brent Geese at the North Bull. Note the two first-year birds in the left foreground with barred wing-coverts.

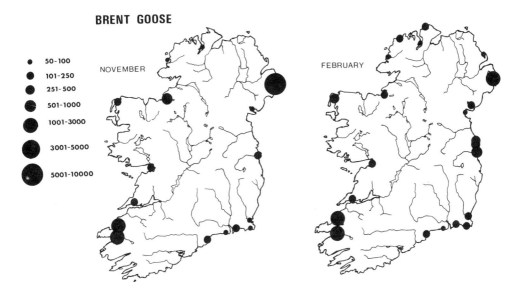

Fig. 40. Principal concentrations of Brent Geese in Ireland in November and February. Conventions are as in Fig. 24.

Barnacle Goose *Branta leucopsis*

The other common black goose, the Barnacle Goose, is very easily identified by its combination of white face and forehead, black crown, neck and breast and grey upperparts with white-edged black bars. In Ireland it is now very much a bird of the islands off the west coast.

Barnacle Geese breed in north-east Greenland, Svalbard (Spitzbergen) and Novaya Zemlya and winter in Ireland, Britain and on the North Sea coast of continental Europe. Irish wintering birds appear to originate exclusively in east Greenland.

The results of several aerial censuses of the Irish wintering population over the years from 1959 to 1973 and some data from a study of the species on the Inishkea Islands, Co. Mayo, have recently been published (Cabot and West 1973). The results of the censuses are summarised in the accompanying table (Table 33). The largest numbers are concentrated on the Inishkea Islands; the remaining birds are scattered in small flocks mainly on islands on the west and north-west coasts (Fig. 41).

The number of juvenile birds as a percentage of the total has fluctuated between 1.2% and 13.7% on the Inishkeas during 1960-1972. These proportions of juvenile birds are very low when compared with the productivity of White-fronted and Brent Geese. However, the mortality rate is also very low. The low productivity of the Inishkea Barnacle Geese is surprising for the Scottish population has doubled since 1961 (Boyd 1968). Cabot and West suggested that the Irish and Scottish wintering birds may breed in different parts of Greenland and that this may account for the differing degree of breeding success. Alternatively, they postulated that the availability of food on the Inishkeas may limit breeding success.

The Inishkea Islands have been uninhabited since 1932 and the build-up of geese appears to date from then. In 1939-40 there were 500-1,000 geese; in 1951-51 there were about 1,200 and by 1954-55 there were estimated to be 2,000 birds (Cabot and West 1973). Prior to the evacuation of the islands there was a large population in the vicinity of Termoncarragh Lake on the Mullet nearby. The effect of security from disturbance has also been demonstrated at Lissadell, Co. Sligo where the numbers have increased steadily since the area was protected from shooting and disturbance and a hide constructed.

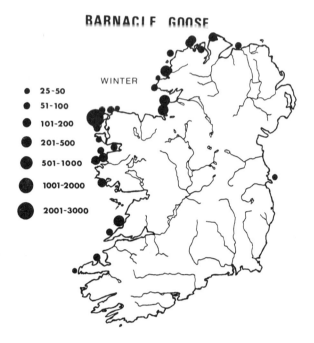

BARNACLE GOOSE

WINTER

● 25-50
● 51-100
● 101-200
● 201-500
● 501-1000
● 1001-2000
● 2001-3000

Fig. 41. Principal concentrations of Barnacle Geese in Ireland in winter. Conventions are as in Fig. 24.

Mute Swan *Cygnus olor*

The Mute Swan is a bird almost everybody knows. Its large size, semi-tameness and abundance at all seasons bring it to the public notice. It differs from the other, wilder swan species in carrying its neck more gracefully, cocking its tail and having an orange bill with a prominent black knob. Juvenile birds are pale brownish and have greyish bills without the knob.

Mute Swans breed commonly in the Baltic region, central Europe and across Asia from the Black Sea to east Siberia as well as in Ireland and Britain.

The species breeds throughout the country except for land above 300

metres where nesting is rare (Sharrock 1976). Unfortunately, no data has been published on the results of a census of breeding swans carried out in 1976. In Britain a

Table 33
Results of censuses of Barnacle Geese in Ireland

Month and Year	Inishkea Islands	Other Locations	Total
December 1959	1,200	1,571	2,771
March 1961	2,300	1,864	4,164
April 1962	2,500	1,904	4,404
March 1966	2,600	2,118	4,718
March 1973	1,980	2,417	4,397
April 1978	2,100	3,650	5,750

census in 1955 showed that there were slightly more than two non-breeders for every breeding pair in England and Wales and an even higher proportion of non-breeders in Scotland (Sharrock 1976).

In late summer Mute Swans congregate at favoured lakes and bays to moult. The location of some of these areas is shown on the map (Fig. 42) but there are certainly many more, especially haunts of small numbers. Most disperse from September onwards and smaller flocks are found at a greater number of sites.

Ogilvie (1972) estimated that the Irish population numbered 5,000-6,000 birds. From a review of the numbers concentrated in large flocks in late summer, and bearing in mind the absence of data for many sites where swans occur this would seem to be a reasonable estimate.

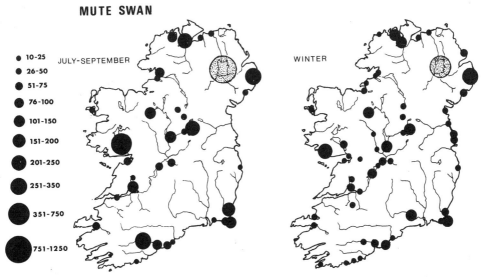

MUTE SWAN

- 10-25
- 26-50
- 51-75
- 76-100
- 101-150
- 151-200
- 201-250
- 251-350
- 351-750
- 751-1250

JULY-SEPTEMBER

WINTER

Fig. 42. Principal concentrations of Mute Swans in Ireland in July-September and winter. Conventions are as in Fig. 24. Many smaller sites are probably omitted.

Whooper Swan *Cygnus cygnus*

Whooper Swans can be distinguished from Mute Swans by the colour of the bill, which has a long yellow base and a black tip, and their general posture. They usually hold the neck straighter and lack the longer, pointed tail of the Mute Swan. Whoopers also call frequently, a loud, ringing 'whoop' note. The features which distinguish them from Bewick's Swans are discussed under that species.

The nominate race breeds in Iceland, northern Scandinavia, Russia and northern Asia, wintering south to France and, in small numbers, to the Mediterranean. Another race, known as the Trumpeter Swan, occurs in North America.

In Ireland this is now the most abundant wintering wild swan. During the last century the Bewick's Swan is said to have outnumbered this species, but by 1950 the situation had reversed (Ruttledge 1974). In Cos. Galway, Mayo and Cavan Whooper

Whooper Swans at Kilcolman, Co. Cork

Swans suddenly appeared on a widespread scale in the early 1940s. The species now occurs commonly in winter throughout the midlands and west of Ireland and in small numbers in Munster and the east coast counties. The preferred habitats include turloughs, broad, slow-moving rivers and shallow lakes. Particularly large flocks, often numbering over 100 birds, are found near Lough Swilly, in the Lough Oughter system and in the Shannon valley. The distribution of this species and the Bewick's Swan has been summarised by Ruttledge (1974).

The first immigrants arrive early in October, sometimes in September, and departure is in March and April. Over 1,000 have been recorded on occasion in October near Lough Swilly. A few birds spend the summer in Ireland. In 1972 a male Whooper Swan bred with a Mute Swan on Lough Corrib and produced young. Breeding together may have occurred for several years previously in the same place (Ruttledge 1975). In July 1976 one was apparently mated to a Mute Swan on a lake on Inishmore, Co. Galway.

Ringing results show that our wintering birds originate in Iceland. The size of the winter population is difficult to estimate but is probably between 4,000 and 6,000 birds.

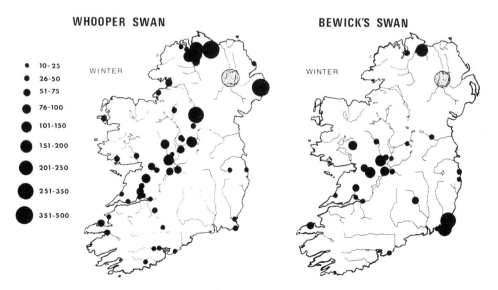

Fig. 43. Principal concentrations of Whooper and Bewick's Swans in Ireland in winter. Conventions are as in Fig. 24. Many smaller sites, especially of Whooper Swans, west of the Shannon are believed to be omitted.

Bewick's Swans and Coots

Bewick's Swan *Cygnus bewickii*

The Bewick's Swan resembles the Whooper much more than the Mute Swan, but differs in being smaller, shorter-necked and rather more goose-like in appearance. The bill is shorter and the yellow area is much more limited in extent than on the Whooper Swan.

This is a scarce swan, now one of Europe's scarcest wildfowl species. It breeds in Arctic Russia and Siberia and winters mainly in Ireland, Britain, north Germany and Denmark. The European wintering population is currently estimated at 9,000 birds (Merne *in litt*).

The Irish distribution has been described in detail by Merne (1977) who estimated a total of 2,000 birds in winter 1975-76. Arrival is in late October, the first birds usually a little later than the first Whoopers, though there have been exceptional records as early as late September. Departure is from mid-February to the end of March.

The main concentrations are at the Wexford Slobs, where the birds favour potatoes, the Shannon valley, several turloughs in Co. Galway, Lough Neagh and the Lough Swilly and Lough Foyle area. During the 1975-76 survey by Merne, coverage of Lough Neagh was poor so the total population may have been as high as 2,500 birds.

The species is extremely sensitive to cold spells: following cold weather in Britain birds have been seen arriving on the Wicklow coast in several winters (Hutchinson 1975).

There has been a considerable change in status over the years since 1900 when the Bewick's Swan was considered to be more numerous than the Whooper (Ussher and Warren 1900). By 1954 Whooper Swans had increased and outnumbered the Bewick's, though it is not known whether Bewick's Swans had actually decreased. There was a marked influx in February 1956 due to cold weather on the continent, but numbers returned to normal, and there were further influxes in 1961-62 and 1962-63. Following these, there was an increase in wintering numbers at several sites and a further, more general increase in 1970-71. Merne (1977) calculated that this may have resulted in a doubling of numbers between 1956 and 1971-72. The flock in Wexford has built up since 1969-70.

Rare Geese

A further five species of geese have been recorded in Ireland. The Lesser White-fronted Goose *Anser erythropus* has only been recorded once, in Wexford in 1969. The Bean Goose *Anser fabalis,* though said to have been common in the nineteenth century, possibly due to confusion with the young of the White-fronted Goose, is now one of the rarest Irish geese. Only 11 have been identified since 1955. The Pink-footed Goose *Anser brachyrhynchus* is an annual winter visitor in very small numbers, mostly to the Wexford Slobs where up to ten occur each year. A few also occur at widely scattered sites in October and November in most years. The Snow Goose *Anser caerulescens* is a rare vagrant. Up to the end of 1976 there had been four records of the white phase Lesser Snow Goose *A. c. caerulescens* and a long series of records of the blue phase, mainly on the Wexford Slobs where at least one, and up to three, have been recorded in most winters since 1945-46. The Greater Snow Goose *A. a. atlanticus* is very rare, having been recorded on two occasions, but some of the 25 records of unidentified Snow Geese may refer to this race. The Canada Goose *Branta canadensis* is an introduced species breeding mainly around Cork city and Strangford Lough (Merne 1970). Since 1960 there have been records each year on the Wexford Slobs of birds belonging to one or more of the smaller races of the Canada Goose and almost certainly of wild origin.

WADERS

Waders have resolved the problem of dealing with wetlands in quite a different way from the majority of ducks, geese and swans. As their name implies they locate their food by wading on relatively long legs through the usually shallow water. Many also have longish, narrow bills for probing in the mud. A total of 57 species has been recorded in Ireland, but four of them have not been thoroughly surveyed for reasons explained later in the text, 17 are scarce visitors from Europe or Asia and 18 are vagrants from North America. This leaves 18 species which are discussed in detail in this chapter.

Our knowledge of the food of waders is still quite sparse. Very little research has been carried out on this aspect of wader biology in Ireland and not much abroad either. Most of the species dealt with in this chapter are shore waders, picking or probing for food at different levels on or below the surface of the mud. Several, however, such as the Lapwing, Golden Plover and Curlew, feed inland in numbers and we know very little about their food.

A flock of Golden Plover probably Ireland's most numerous waders.

The reader of the species accounts which follow will be struck by the qualifications entered against most generalisations and wonder at the value of the survey on which these comments are based. Up to 1971-72 we did not even know which were the most important estuaries for waders, let alone have any idea of the size of the Irish wintering population of any species. Now we know a great deal about our shore waders, probably more than we know about most duck species. The most important estuaries have been censused monthly, with the exception of Cork Harbour for which inadequate data exist. The Irish counts have also coincided with a huge international effort which has enabled us to put the Irish population firmly into its European and north-west African context.

The information collected over the four years of the survey, supplemented by records from the literature, is presented in the following pages in maps and graphs with the same conventions used in the accounts of the ducks.

Ireland's importance for most wader species can be gauged from these accounts. For breeding waders it is not of vital importance, but as a passage and wintering area Ireland is extremely important. Most of the Icelandic breeding population of Golden Plover winters in Ireland and many Icelandic Black-tailed Godwits and Redshanks do so as well. The Irish wintering populations of Bar-tailed Godwits and Redshanks are about 15% of the European wintering populations. Although quite small, the Irish Sanderling population of at least 2,000 birds may be as much as 20% of the European population. In hard weather there is no doubt that Ireland is of even greater importance, particularly for Lapwing and Golden Plover.

Oystercatcher *Haematopus ostralegus*

Oystercatchers are large, noisy and very conspicuous black and white waders. The upperparts are black, including the head and breast, and the underparts pure white. The bill is stout and long, and very striking because of its red coloration. The legs are also red. In flight Oystercatchers show a white wing-bar and rump which contrast sharply with the black mantle, wing-coverts and head. The call is a loud piping, most often heard from birds in flight.

The race which occurs in Ireland, *H.o. ostralegus,* breeds on the coast in Iceland, the Faeroes, across northern Europe and in Asia Minor. Other races occur in the Canary Isles, South Africa, Asia, America and Australasia. In winter the population of Europe and north-west Africa is estimated to be about 563,000 birds, almost 90% of which are concentrated in Britain, the Netherlands and Ireland (Prater 1976b).

The Irish breeding population is almost completely coastal. Sharrock (1976) postulated an average of 20 pairs per 10-km square with confirmed or probable

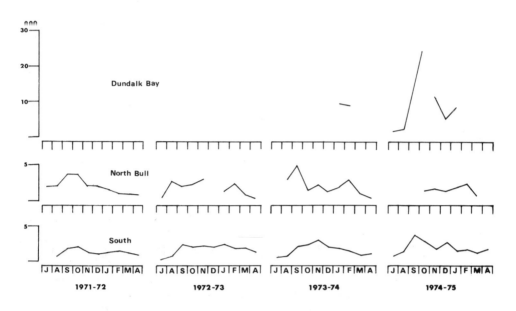

Fig. 44. Numbers of Oystercatchers at Dundalk Bay, the North Bull and south coast wetlands, 1971-72 to 1974-75. Counts of Dundalk Bay are incomplete.

breeding in Britain and Ireland during the years from 1968 to 1972. On this basis the Irish breeding population would be in excess of 3,500 pairs, which compares with Dare's estimate (1966) of 4,000 pairs on the west, north and north-east coasts, itself based on an assumption of two pairs per mile of coast, excluding Sligo, and two pairs per island. Dare considered that 150-250 pairs breed on the east and south coasts, chiefly in Dublin and Wexford, and 5-15 pairs inland.

The movements of Irish bred Oystercatchers are almost completely unknown. If their movements are similar to those of birds bred in Wales, just across the Irish Sea, then some would remain in Ireland and others move south to France and Iberia (Dare 1970). The handful of recoveries of Oystercatchers ringed as young in Ireland would lend support to this. They include a single bird ringed in Co. Down as a chick and recovered in Spain in October and a couple, also ringed as chicks in Co. Down, recovered in November and April locally.

At the coastal estuaries and bays the summering flocks of drab, non-breeding Oystercatchers are augmented by adults in bright breeding plumage from mid-July and there is a steady increase in numbers to a peak usually in September (Fig. 44) The largest numbers of all are recorded at Dundalk Bay where up to 26,000 have been counted. In general, much the largest numbers are recorded on the east and south coasts (Fig. 45). In the north and west, apart from Lough Foyle and the west Kerry bays, Oystercatchers are thinly, albeit widely, dispersed. Numbers are lower in

December when the Irish wintering population is probably in the region of 30,000-35,000 birds, but there is return passage in spring. This is noticeable at the North Bull in February and March and on the south coast as late as March and April. In May and June flocks of non-breeding birds are present in all the estuaries. Since Oystercatchers do not breed until their third or fourth year it is not surprising that these flocks frequently number several hundred birds.

The Irish wintering population consists of Scottish, Icelandic and Faeroese breeding birds and, most likely, Irish breeders as well. Since some Oystercatchers are back on their breeding grounds in Aberdeen in January and February (Heppleston 1971) it seems likely that the increase in numbers in this month on the east coast involves Scottish breeders. Dare (1970) pointed out that Oystercatchers are later returning to the Shetlands, the Faeroes and Norway. Most do not return to the Faeroes until the second half of March and those breeding in the extreme north-east of Norway are often not back until the end of April. It may be that the late spring increase on the south coast of Ireland involves an influx of birds returning to a far north breeding area such as Iceland.

The winter distribution of Oystercatchers reflects the distribution of large sandy expanses where cockles *Cardium edule,* the preferred prey item, and mussels *Mytilus edulis* proliferate. Hence, very few are seen in the muddy Shannon estuary, but enormous numbers occur in Dundalk Bay. Indeed, O'Connor and Brown (1977), in a study of Oystercatchers at Strangford Lough, showed that the birds there seriously depleted cockle stocks in autumn, particularly in regional areas, and by January they tended to congregate into a few good sites.

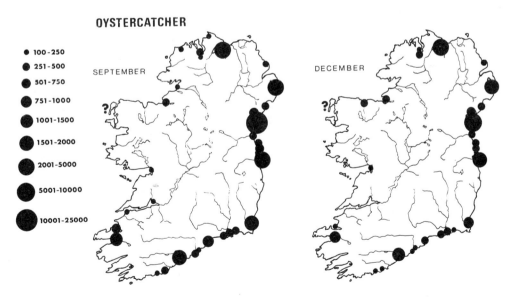

*Fig. 45. Principal concentrations of Oystercatchers in Ireland in September and December.
Conventions are as in Fig. 24.*

Lapwing *Vanellus vanellus*

Lapwing must be among the most familiar Irish waders as they breed quite widely, though rather thinly, and from autumn to spring flocks occur all over the country. The birds are very distinctive. In flight they look rather like crows with white bellies because of their dark, rounded wings and slow flight. On the ground Lapwing are dark greenish above and show a characteristic topknot.

They breed in the Faeroes and from Scandinavia south to the Mediterranean as well as in parts of central Asia and Siberia. There is substantial migration in autumn as many birds move west or south, but no estimate of the western European breeding or wintering population has been made.

Lapwing breed over much of Ireland, but are peculiarly scarce south-west of a line from Lough Derg to Wexford. Nobody really knows how many breed in Ireland, but we do know that their numbers collapsed after the severe winter of 1962-63. At 17 sites in Kerry where a total of 134 pairs bred in 1962 only nine pairs bred in 1963. In 1972 a total of 76 pairs was counted, still only 57% of the total in 1962 (F. King *in litt.*).

The first Lapwing to appear at the fringe of wetlands after early summer arrive in

Lapwing on estuarine mud.

the second week of June and there is a build-up in July and August. Flocks of over 500 birds are scarce at this time. There is a much more rapid increase in October and extremely large numbers of Lapwing are present from November to February. Numbers decline quite quickly from late February and flocks of only a couple of hundred or so remain at the end of March. Some of these indeed may be Irish breeding birds.

The numbers of Lapwing in Ireland from November to March are massive. The map (Fig. 46) only illustrates the distribution of flocks at wetlands. Large flocks also occur widely on pasture and rough land around bogs. The total Irish population in December certainly exceeds 100,000 and might well exceed 250,000.

Many Lapwing have been ringed throughout Europe and their recoveries are the subject of a remarkable paper by Imboden (1974) which analyses at great length the movements of these birds. He concludes that Ireland is the wintering area for many Lapwings breeding in northern England and central Scotland, adults tending to be more numerous than juveniles. Some Scandinavian birds and a very few Belgian, Dutch and German birds also winter here. In early summer some Lapwing leave their breeding areas in central Europe and move westwards, some reaching Britain. Whether many of them reach Ireland, or the early autumn build-up here involves British birds only is unknown. The species is extremely sensitive to cold weather, wintering west and south of the 3° C January isotherm. During spells of exceptionally hard weather on the continent flocks can be observed flying in across the Irish Sea all day and the numbers present throughout the country increase dramatically. When the weather eases birds disappear, presumably returning eastwards again.

Unfortunately, we know nothing of the movements of Irish breeding Lapwing. There is room here, as with so many of our native breeding waders, for an interesting study.

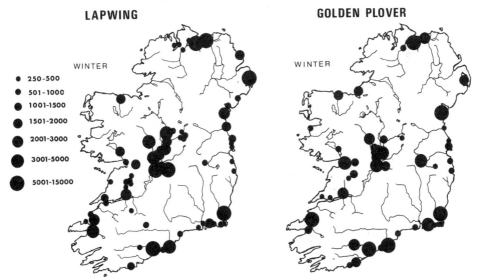

Fig. 46. Principal reported concentrations of Lapwing and Golden Plover in Ireland in winter. Conventions are as in Fig. 24. Many flocks have certainly gone unreported.

Ringed Plover *Charadrius hiaticula*

Ringed Plovers are delightful little waders, sandy brown above and white below, with a black breast-band, white throat and black and white patterning on the head. Their dumpy bodies, confiding habits and preference for sandy beaches much frequented by the public are probably responsible for their popularity.

There are several races. Irish breeding birds belong to the nominate race which breeds in Greenland and western Europe south of the Baltic. The Irish wintering population is drawn from the north-west European breeding birds. Those wintering in Africa are mainly from the northerly populations of Greenland, northern Scandinavia, north-western U.S.S.R. and Iceland, most of which are of the race *C. h. tundrae* which has been identified in Ireland on autumn passage. Another race occurs in North America. The wintering population in Europe and north-west Africa has been estimated at 43,000 birds (Prater 1976b) but as many birds are scattered on small beaches rarely visited by wader counters this is probably an underestimate.

Ringed Plovers breed around the Irish coastline wherever there are sandy or shingle beaches. In the west they breed in a variety of sites, sometimes on turf above sea-cliffs and on salt marsh. Inland they nest around a number of lakes in the midlands and west, at Lough Neagh and at the Lee reservoirs in Co. Cork. In a census in 1975, 93 pairs were found in Northern Ireland (Prater 1976c). In Dublin and Wicklow the breeding population has been estimated at 30-60 pairs (Hutchinson 1975) and in Wexford at 50+ (O. J. Merne *in litt.*). No estimate of the total Irish breeding population has ever been published but it probably exceeds 2,000 pairs.

Early each autumn Ringed Plovers congregate in flocks at estuaries and beaches around the coast. Flocks of 200-300 are widespread in July, much more widespread than the map of winter distribution would suggest (Fig. 47). On the west coast particularly, these parties are widespread. In August the flocks are larger and up to 300 together may be counted at most coastal lagoons and estuaries; small parties even occur inland. Adults greatly outnumber juveniles at this time, at least on the south coast. Numbers are slightly lower in September, but there is a much higher proportion of juveniles on the south coast and perhaps elsewhere. After September numbers appear to stabilise and flocks are resident on the sandier parts of estuaries and beaches all around the country. The map represents this distribution fairly accurately, though a large number of small parties on the west coast, and perhaps the north-west, were probably missed. In spring there is no noticeable passage at any estuaries.

The two European races of Ringed Plovers can be separated by measurement in the

hand. The Arctic breeding
C. h. tundrae birds are
smaller and also slightly
darker than the
populations of *C. h.
hiaticula*. In winter it
appears that all or almost
all of our birds are of the
nominate race. In autumn
birds of both races are
known to occur, the
Arctic on their passage
south to Africa. But
nobody really knows as
yet the proportion of birds
from each race which
occur during the autumn.
Even the origins of the
winter population are little
known, though some Irish

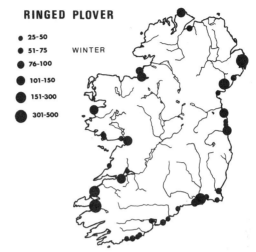

Fig. 47. Principal concentrations of Ringed Plover in Ireland in winter.
Conventions are as in Fig. 24

and British bred Ringed Plovers have been recovered here in winter. The total of the wintering population is difficult to estimate as so many winter on little watched beaches but is probably between 5,000 and 10,000 birds.

Grey Plover *Pluvialis squatarola*

This is probably the least known of the commoner plovers. It is quite a widely distributed winter visitor and passage migrant, but normally in very small numbers. Although it resembles the Golden Plover this species is greyer and drabber in winter plumage; it is also rather larger and stouter. In flight the white rump and conspicuous black axillaries are diagnostic.

The Grey Plover is one of the most widespread waders in the world, breeding in Arctic Russia, Siberia and America and wintering on the coasts of Europe, Africa, southern Asia, North and South America and Australia. The European and north-west African wintering population has been estimated at 43,000 birds (Prater 1976b).

None nest in Ireland, but a few birds sometimes spend the summer on the coast. The autumn migration begins in July, and sometimes even mid-June at particularly favoured sites like the North Bull (Hutchinson 1975), and there is a build-up of numbers in the autumn, especially on the south coast. Thereafter, the pattern of occurrences at different sites is very puzzling. On the south coast there is clearly a substantial autumn passage in October with a decrease normally in November, though in 1974-75 the decrease appears to have been delayed until January (Fig. 49). Then there is a spring passage, with a peak in February and March (Fig. 49). On the east coast, counts at the North Bull indicate much smaller autumn numbers which may represent the arrival of wintering birds rather than passage migration. But there is a spring peak there as well. On the Fergus estuary, Co. Clare the largest numbers occur at this time. When the totals on the south coast are broken down over estuaries, as on the map, it can be seen that even on the south coast numbers are higher in December at some sites. Whether these fluctuations are merely inter-estuarine feeding movements or part of a larger scale migration is not known.

Overall, however, it seems likely that some non-breeding birds remain to summer in western Europe and that others move south-west in autumn from the breeding area in northern Russia. Some which reach Ireland remain to winter; others move farther south in Europe or into Africa. In spring the return of these birds may well cause the increase in February and March so noticeable on the graph.

The Irish wintering population is probably between 750 and 1,500 birds.

Golden Plover *Pluvialis apricarius*

Almost as well known as the Lapwing, the Golden Plover is almost as widespread in winter and often occurs in even larger flocks. But the species is very different in appearance. Golden Plover are very fast flying birds with narrow pointed wings and a

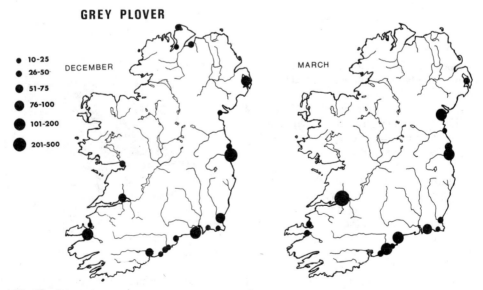

GREY PLOVER

- 10-25
- 26-50
- 51-75
- 76-100
- 101-200
- 201-500

DECEMBER

MARCH

Fig. 48. Principal concentrations of Grey Plover in Ireland in December and March. Conventions are as in Fig. 24.

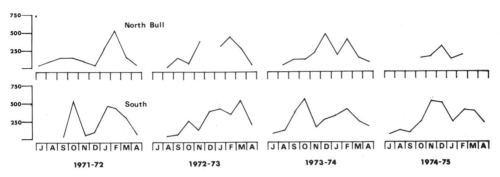

Fig. 49. Numbers of Grey Plover at the North Bull and at south coast wetlands, 1971-72 to 1974-75.

whistling flight. In colour they appear mottled golden-brown above and whitish below in winter. In summer the upperparts are brighter and the underparts have a large black patch on the belly which extends to a varying extent up onto the face and throat.

The nominate race nests in Ireland, Britain and around the Baltic. The race *P. a. altifrons* breeds in Iceland, northern Europe and northern Siberia. Both subspecies move south in the winter. No estimate has ever been published of the numbers wintering in Europe.

The Irish breeding population is very small and concentrated in west Galway, west Mayo, Donegal and Antrim. The total involved has been estimated at 600 pairs (Sharrock 1976). No study has ever been made of their breeding biology or movements. If their behaviour is similar to that of the British breeding birds Irish Golden Plover return to the nesting grounds in February and early March and remain until July when the first parties of resident birds move to the lowlands to spend the winter (Ratcliffe 1976).

However, the overwhelming majority of Irish wintering Golden Plover are immigrants. The first very small parties appear in early September, only occasional birds being seen in August. But the real immigration is in October and November when flocks of over 10,000 birds are regular at Ballymacoda, Co. Cork, Dundalk Bay, Co. Louth, the Little Brosna, Co. Offaly and on the river Suck in Co. Roscommon. These large flocks seem to break up into smaller ones for the winter and these are widespread, much more so than the map (Fig. 46), which is based only on observations at wetlands, would suggest. The number present in winter is probably in excess of 200,000 birds. Many disperse in February and March, presumably returning towards their breeding area, and there are some indications of a further arrival in March and April, but very few remain into May. Many flocks in late spring are of birds in summer plumage and all show the characters of *P. a altifrons*.

Ringing recoveries of this species in Europe have been studied by Norrevang (1959) and he concluded that Icelandic birds winter mainly in Ireland, to a lesser extent in Britain and with a few moving as far south as Iberia. More than half of the Icelandic foreign ringing recoveries were in Ireland. Conversely, there were no recoveries in Ireland of Golden Plover, presumably from the north-east, ringed on migration in the Netherlands.

Golden Plover

Turnstone *Arenaria interpres*

Turnstones are common but rather inconspicuous waders of stony and rocky shores. The mottled dark brown upperparts and blackish breast-band merge well into a background of rocks and seaweed. The throat and belly are white, the legs orange and the bill dark. In summer the upperparts are much brighter and more orange and the head acquires a black and white pattern. At all seasons Turnstones can immediately be recognised in flight by their combination of small size and bold black and white markings.

The nominate race breeds from Greenland east to Siberia, extending in Europe as far south as Denmark, and winters south to southern Africa and Australia. A second race occurs in North America. Prater (1976b) estimated the wintering population in Europe and north-west Africa at 23,000 birds, but this is probably a substantial under-estimate: most Turnstones winter on rocky or stony shores where wader counters do not survey them. Prater's estimate for Ireland of 1,000 birds is certainly very much below the real figure which is probably well in excess of 5,000.

Unfortunately, as Turnstones prefer non-estuarine coasts we have relatively little data on them. A few non-breeders remain to summer at many points around the coast. In July the first immigrants arrive and peak autumn passage is in August and

September. Numbers are slightly lower in winter on the south and east coasts but there is a marked spring passage in late March and April. On the north coast numbers are generally highest in mid-winter. With the exception of Snipe. Turnstones are probably the least accurately counted common waders as even in estuaries they tend to be missed when roosting on rocky islands or even buoys in a channel.

Curlew *Numenius arquata*

This is probably the best known of all Irish wading birds. Its plaintive 'cur-lew' call can be heard on damp ground, and sometimes on pasture land, almost anywhere in Ireland from autumn through until spring. In summer it is not quite so widespread. The Curlew is a large streaky brown bird, the largest of our waders, with a long, decurved bill. The only bird with which it can be confused is the Whimbrel and the main differences are described in the account of that species.

The race concerned, *N. a. arquata*, breeds in Europe east to Russia and extends into western Asia. In winter it reaches as far as South Africa. A separate race occurs in Siberia. Counts on estuaries in western Europe and north-west Africa have been used to estimate a total winter population of 150,000 birds in the region (Prater 1976b) but the great majority of the birds occur inland. The total for Ireland of 15,000 used in this calculation is very much lower than the real total of those wintering on estuaries, let alone those wintering inland.

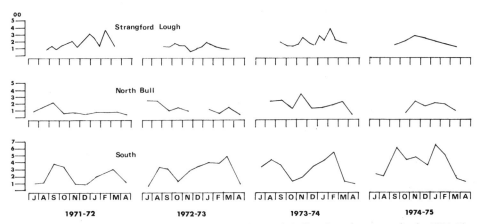

Fig. 50. Numbers of Curlews at Strangford Lough, the North Bull and south coast wetlands, 1971-72 to 1974-75.

Curlews breed throughout most of Ireland. They are scarcest in west Kerry, south Cork and Wexford and commonest in the drumlin belt of the north (Sharrock 1976). Some birds, presumably too young to breed, remain in flocks on the coast for the summer but the numbers are small, certainly smaller than the flocks of non-breeding Oystercatchers at this time. In July numbers increase at many sites on the coast and, at least on the south coast, there is a fairly obvious increase to an August and September peak (Fig. 50). On the east coast, at Strangford Lough and the North Bull, for example, there is no real evidence of any autumn passage: the monthly fluctuations are remarkably haphazard and may be related primarily to local movements of birds to and from fields in the vicinity of the estuaries. In the south there is a clear decline in winter, followed by an increase in February and March which is also discernible at Strangford Lough and the North Bull. Most birds have left wetlands by the end of March and numbers from April to the end of June are quite low.

From ringing recoveries it appears that very large numbers of Scottish, northern English and Scandinavian bred Curlews winter in Ireland, almost certainly together with many Irish bred birds. As most Curlews have vacated the breeding areas in Britain by late July (Sharrock 1976) it is likely that many of these birds move west quite early to Ireland. Indeed, at least five have been recovered in August in the year in which they were ringed as chicks, and one ringed on 5th June in Inverness as a chick was recovered on 31st July in Co. Galway, clear evidence of quite rapid movement. There have also been three recoveries in June of birds ringed as chicks in northern Britain between February and early April

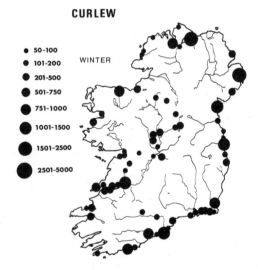

CURLEW

●	50-100
●	101-200
●	201-500
●	501-750
●	751-1000
●	1001-1500
●	1501-2500
●	2501-5000

WINTER

Fig. 51. Principal reported concentrations of Curlews in Ireland in winter.
Conventions are as in Fig. 24.
Many flocks have certainly gone unreported.

(Sharrock 1976) and the peak in the counts at most Irish sites in February and March clearly relates to birds congregating together at wetlands prior to returning to breed. Whether birds actually arrive in Ireland from farther south is unknown. There is a massive and very noisy nocturnal movement in March noted in most years on the east coast in Dublin and Wexford, presumably of birds returning to Scotland and northern England.

The mid-winter population is probably between 50,000 and 150,000 birds. One cannot be any more precise.

Whimbrel *Numenius phaeopus*

The Whimbrel is remarkably similar to the Curlew in appearance. The most obvious differentiating feature is the call which in this species is a rapid 'titti-titti-titti-titti-titti-tit'. The Whimbrel is also slightly smaller, has a proportionately shorter bill and two broad, dark stripes on the crown.

The European race *N. p. phaeopus* nests in northern Europe and north-west Asia, and winters mainly in Africa. The Hudsonian Whimbrel *N. p. hudsonicus* breeds in North America. It has been recorded once in Ireland. A third race breeds in north-east Asia.

A very few Whimbrels breed in Scotland but there is no evidence of nesting having been attempted in Ireland where the species is primarily a passage migrant. Spring passage usually begins in early April, when the first few birds arrive, though there have been records of presumed migrants in March, but the peak passage is in the last week of April and the first two weeks of May. Very large numbers are involved in some years, particularly on the south coast, and 1969 was the best year in the recent past. At Ballycotton, Co. Cork a total of 549 was counted on 27th April, most of which

Black-tailed Godwits

were seen flying in from the sea. Large numbers were also recorded at Roche's Point, Co. Cork and in Co. Wexford in the same period, and in Co. Dublin the largest parties recorded in recent years (up to 64 in a flock) were noted. Although fewer were recorded in Co. Cork in 1970 (maximum of 120 at Ballycotton) and passage in Wexford was virtually non-existent this was an unprecedented spring in Kerry with many flocks of 200-300 birds near Tralee.

Spring passage is much less noticeable on the north coast, but very large numbers occur inland at times, as the record of 1,100 roosting at Kineagh turlough, Co. Roscommon in late April 1973 illustrates. From these records it appears that the main Whimbrel immigration to Ireland is on a relatively narrow front, in some years further to the west than in others. And in some years so few are seen as to suggest that the large flocks have either flown over Ireland or moved north through Britain to the east.

A few Whimbrels spend the summer, mainly on the south coast, and return migration begins in June and reaches a peak in August. Numbers in September are lower and a few still remain as late as early November. Flocks are generally much smaller than in spring but the birds remain for much longer periods. Single birds and tiny parties are very widely dispersed. A few birds remain to winter on the Cork coast every year, especially in Cork Harbour.

Black-tailed Godwit *Limosa limosa*

Godwits are large waders, smaller than Curlews but larger than Redshanks, with long legs and long, straight or faintly up-curved bills. In winter they are coloured much as Curlews; in summer plumage they are much brighter with a chestnut head, neck and breast. The Black-tailed Godwit is distinguished from the Bar-tailed Godwit by several features, the most obvious of which are noticeable in flight — the broad white wing-bars, white rump and tail with a black terminal band and long legs extending beyond the tail. On the ground the Black-tailed Godwit shows longer legs, a  longer bill and darker and more uniform upperparts.

Two races occur in Europe. The race *L. l. islandica* breeds in Iceland and winters mainly in Europe. The nominate race breeds in continental Europe and western Asia and winters mainly in Africa. It has been estimated that the Icelandic race has a population of 30-40,000, perhaps as many as 60,000, and the nominate race a minimum of 140,000 in the western part of its range (Prater 1976b). A third race occurs in north-east Asia.

Although Britain has been recolonised since 1952 and over 60 pairs were nesting in 1972, mostly in England, there is no evidence that birds have ever nested in Ireland. This is somewhat surprising as many more winter here than in England.

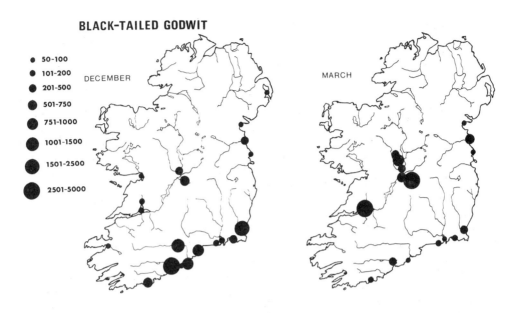

BLACK-TAILED GODWIT

- 50-100
- 101-200
- 201-500
- 501-750
- 751-1000
- 1001-1500
- 1501-2500
- 2501-5000

DECEMBER

MARCH

Fig. 52. Principal concentrations of Black-tailed Godwits in Ireland in December and March. Conventions are as in Fig. 24.

The first autumn Black-tailed Godwits appear in Ireland as early as the end of June. There is then a slow build-up in numbers until mid-August when the peak passage commences. This is quite brief and does not extend beyond the first ten days of September. Indeed, it seems unlikely that many Black-tailed Godwits arrive in Ireland at all after this sudden immigration, but few of these immigrants appear to depart before October and then only a relatively small proportion leave. The majority of Black-tailed Godwits have left Iceland by mid-August (J. Wilson *in litt.*) and most moult their wing-feathers in Ireland. The largest numbers in autumn occur at those estuaries on the south coast which hold most in December, but flocks of 100-200 occur on the east coast and smaller parties at turloughs and callows in the Shannon valley.

In December the largest concentrations are all on the south coast. Cork Harbour (up to 3,500), Wexford Harbour (up to 2,000), Ballymacoda (up to 1,100), Dungarvan Harbour (up to 850, in one winter as many as 1,600) and Clonakilty Bay (up to 900) hold the largest numbers. Black-tailed Godwits appear to prefer muddier estuaries than Bar-tailed Godwits, but in Cork Harbour the two species feed alongside each other. Black-tailed Godwits are quite often found feeding or roosting in damp pastures, a habitat in which Bar-tailed Godwits are very rare.

Departure from the south coast estuaries is remarkably early. A decrease is noticeable in January and numbers are much reduced by February. The map illustrating March distribution indicates the scarcity of Black tailed Godwits in the south and highlights the flocks which now occur in the Shannon valley and estuary. At such sites as the Little Brosna and the River Shannon near Shannon Harbour the species is scarce in late autumn and not until December are the first winter flocks seen. There is a rapid build-up in January to peak numbers in February when flocks can be extremely large. A count of 4,600 on the Little Brosna in February 1975 was large by any standards. Few remain into April. On the Shannon estuary the situation is very different. Here there are very few wintering birds, though there is quite a strong autumn passage (Stapleton 1975) but from mid-March to mid-April enormous numbers occur. In March 1973, 6,500 were recorded on the Fergus estuary alone; in April 1974, 16,400 were counted on the entire estuary. Counts in spring 1975 and 1976 produced maxima of 4,500 and 5,400 respectively. However, given the infrequency of the counts and the brief stay of the birds it is quite possible that much larger numbers were present in these last two years but were absent on the count dates.

Only very small numbers are present from late April to June, mostly at brackish lagoons, but nesting has never been suspected.

Prater (1975) described a remarkable increase in the wintering population of Black-tailed Godwits in England over the past fifty years. Ruttledge (1966) considered that numbers had greatly increased in Ireland during the 1950s and early 1960s. Wintering numbers vary considerably, however, from one year to another, but 1974-75 was an exceptional year with the highest recorded counts at Cork and Wexford Harbours. In general, the winter population is probably in the region of 8,000-10,000 birds.

Bar-tailed Godwit *Limosa lapponica*

The Bar-tailed Godwit is very similar to the Black-tailed Godwit when at rest, but in flight its uniform brown wings, barred tail and relatively short legs distinguish it instantly. On the ground it can be identified with practice by its shorter, more upturned bill and paler upperparts with more noticeable pale edgings to the scapulars and wing-coverts.

The nominate race breeds across northern Europe and Asia from Scandinavia to Siberia and winters in Europe, west Africa and east to the Indian Ocean. Another race occurs in eastern Siberia and Alaska. There are two wintering populations on the Atlantic coast of Europe and north Africa. One, which totals almost 90,000 birds, is centred on Britain, the Netherlands and Ireland; the other, which totals over 200,000 birds, is almost completely confined to the Banc d'Arguin in Mauretania in west Africa (Prater 1976b).

The status of the Bar-tailed Godwit in Ireland is relatively simple to describe. It appears to be a winter visitor, with no evidence of passage migration at all. Prater (1974a) described how the adults migrate west and south-west to the Atlantic coast of Europe in late July and the first two weeks of August to moult after breeding in the area from northern Scandinavia to the Taimyr Peninsula in the Soviet Union. Juvenile birds follow, later in the autumn. The first birds arrive back in Ireland in mid-July, but the main immigration is in August. Whether these birds moult their wing-feathers in Ireland is not known, but almost all have moulted their summer body plumage. Numbers rise slightly in early September, perhaps because of an influx of juveniles, but fluctuations thereafter appear to be relatively limited until the great majority depart between mid-February and mid-March. A few remain as late as May and small flocks of 200-300 birds spend the summer at Lough Foyle and Wexford Harbour, occasionally elsewhere, in most years.

Bar-tailed Godwits prefer sandier estuaries and comparison of the map of December distribution with that for the Oystercatcher shows a marked resemblence. Bar-tailed Godwits feed primarily on lugworms *Arenicola sp.* and Oystercatchers on edible cockles *Cardium edule,* but both thrive on sandier foreshores. The largest numbers occur in Dundalk Bay where 6,000-7,000 winter. Over 3,000 winter at Lough Foyle and over 2,000 in Dublin Bay. The peak mid-winter population is probably between 16,000 and 20,000 birds.

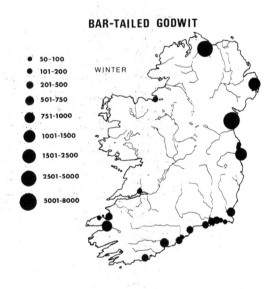

BAR-TAILED GODWIT

- 50-100
- 101-200
- 201-500
- 501-750
- 751-1000
- 1001-1500
- 1501-2500
- 2501-5000
- 5001-8000

WINTER

Fig. 53. Principal concentrations of Bar-tailed Godwits in Ireland in winter.
Conventions are as in Fig. 24.

Common Sandpiper *Tringa hyperleucos*

Unlike the other wader species occurring commonly in Ireland the Common Sandpiper is primarily a summer visitor. Very few birds remain to winter. It is easily identified by its slender, graceful shape, constant dipping of the tail when perched and by its spasmodic flight action of fast wing-beats interspersed with short glides. Its teetering flight-call is utterly distinctive.

The species breeds throughout most of Europe and in Asia east to Japan. It winters in Africa and southern Asia.

In Ireland it breeds in a variety of habitats. East of a line drawn from Belfast to Skibbereen it is thinly distributed and most of the breeding pairs are on upland lakes or fast-flowing rivers. West of this line, in the midlands, Connacht and along the Shannon, Common Sandpipers breed around the rims of low-lying lakes in much higher densities. In the south-west they breed on coastal shingle bars as well (Sharrock 1976). Since not even a sample census has ever been carried out it is impossible to give any estimate of the breeding population. There is, however, some evidence of a decrease since the 1950s in the east of the country (Sharrock 1976).

Immigrants arrive on the coast from about mid-April and are regularly seen until mid-May. Numbers are quite small, the birds almost always occurring singly or in pairs. They move inland quite rapidly to breed, not returning to the coast until the last few days of June. Flocks form from later June and up to 30 together, exceptionally over 50, may be seen at many estuaries and small coastal lagoons in July. Passage reaches a peak in the last week of July and numbers then decline through August. Common Sandpipers are scarce in September and rare in October.

Small numbers winter on the Cork coast every year, perhaps as many as ten wintering in Cork Harbour, and occasional birds as far north as Co. Antrim.

Common Sandpiper

Redshank *Tringa totanus*

The Redshank must be familiar to most Irish people who visit the coast for it is about as widespread as the Oystercatcher and Dunlin. It is a medium-sized, brownish wader with longish red legs and a very conspicuous white bar on each wing. The call is a loud, down-slurred whistle.

Three races occur in western Europe, several others in Asia. *T. t. brittanica,* the population which breeds in Britain and Ireland, winters mainly on the coastline of these islands, though immatures winter as far south as Spain and Portugal. The Icelandic population, *T. t. robusta,* winters in the same area.

The nominate race breeds across most of Europe and extends into Asia. Birds from Scandinavia winter in north and west Africa and southern Europe (Prater 1976b). The western European wintering population has been estimated at 124,000; that of north-west Africa at 110,000 birds (Prater 1976b).

The Irish breeding population is quite small and centred on the Connacht and midland lakes and Lough Neagh. Coastal breeders are quite scarce with none nesting on the coasts of Kerry, Cork or Waterford and only a few in south-east Wexford.

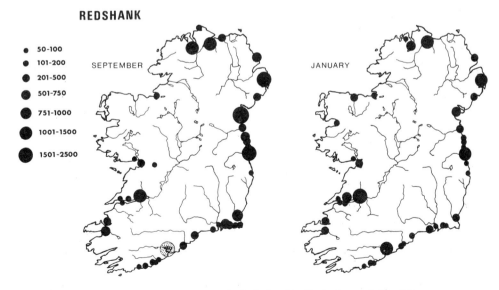

Fig. 54. *Principal concentrations of Redshanks in Ireland in September and January. Conventions are as in Fig. 24.*

Again, it is not possible to make any reasonable estimate of the breeding population because of the absence of any sample census data.

The first Redshanks return to the coastal wetlands in mid-June and between the end of the month and mid-July numbers build up rapidly. Peak autumn numbers are in September or October. At this time of the year long, straggling lines of Redshanks may be seen feeding on almost any estuary in the country. As the map illustrates (Fig. 54) the species is extremely widespread and the map of September distribution probably understates the situation because of the low level of coverage in the west. After the autumn peak, usually in September, numbers decline markedly for the winter before increasing again in February and March and, at least in 1972-73, in April (Fig. 55). Virtually none are seen on the estuaries in May or the first half of June. The counts at the North Bull and on south coast wetlands illustrate these movements well; those for Strangford Lough show much greater fluctuations, which are not easily explained.

Ringing recoveries indicate that Redshanks from northern England, Scotland and Iceland winter in Ireland. Whether the autumn and spring passage includes many continental Redshanks *T. t. totanus* is questionable: at the very least it seems unlikely that many birds moving south from Scandinavia to southern Europe or north-west Africa would migrate as far west as Ireland. Whereas it seems very likely that Icelandic Redshanks, just like Icelandic Black-tailed Godwits, pass through on their way to and from France and Iberia.

Because Redshanks are so numerous, small numbers even being found inland as well as on the coast, the mid-winter population is very difficult to estimate, but is probably between 11,000 and 18,000 birds in January. In September numbers are probably in excess of 30,000.

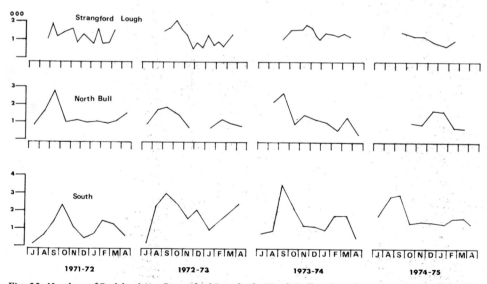

Fig. 55. *Numbers of Redshanks at Strangford Lough, the North Bull and south coast wetlands, 1971-72 to 1974-75.*

Spotted Redshank *Tringa erythropus*

As its name suggests the Spotted Redshank resembles the Redshank in general appearance and in its red legs. In winter it is a slightly greyer bird; in summer it is unmistakeable in its black plumage spotted with white on the back. In all plumages it can be identified in flight by trailing red legs and its lack of any white wing-bar. On the ground the bill and legs look longer than those of the Redshank. The call, a disyllabic 'chu-wit', is diagnostic.

The species breeds in northern Europe and Siberia and migrates south to winter primarily in the Mediterranean area and southern Africa. Numbers wintering in north-west Africa are very low and provisional figures for the Mediterranean coastline suggest a figure of only 800 birds.

Spotted Redshanks were rare passage migrants and very rare winter visitors in Ireland up to 1952 (Kennedy *et al* 1954). They are now regular autumn passage migrants and small numbers spend the winter. The first autumn migrants usually appear in late July and there is a steady passage in August, September and October when small parties or several single birds are usually present at a number of south coast wetlands and quite sizeable flocks in Wexford Harbour. Peak counts in Wexford Harbour in recent years were of 71 in 1971, 75 in 1972, 105 in 1973, 50 in 1974 and 70 in 1975.

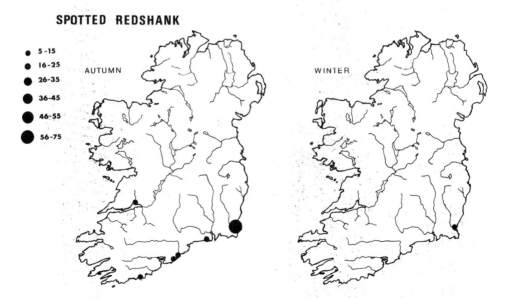

Fig. 56. Principal concentrations of Spotted Redshanks in Ireland in autumn and winter. Conventions are as in Fig. 24.

Numbers decline after mid-October but a few winter at a number of sites on the south coast and in the south-west. The only large party is at Wexford Harbour. The total winter population probably fluctuates between 25 and 50 birds.

Passage in spring is lighter than in autumn, and extends from the end of February to the beginning of May. Only a very few birds appear to be involved. In Co. Cork there is an arrival in most years of birds in summer plumage in June and up to eight birds have been recorded at Ballycotton in June or July. These are obviously non-breeders.

Greenshank *Tringa nebularia*

The Greenshank is a larger and much greyer bird than the Redshank. On the ground the underparts look very white, the head and neck pale grey and the upperparts generally a slightly darker grey. The bill is lightly upturned and the legs long and greenish-grey. In flight the wings look very dark and contrast with the white lower back and rump. The call is a triple whistle: 'tew-tew-tew'.

The breeding range is quite northerly and extends from Scotland east across northern Europe and Asia. In winter Greenshanks occur in quite small numbers in Britain and Ireland (*c.* 700), Portugal (*c.* 100) and north-west Africa (*c.* 1,200) (Prater 1976b), but the main wintering area appears to be farther south in Africa.

This is one of Ireland's rarest breeding birds. One pair nested in Connacht in 1972 and 1974, and probably in 1971 as well.

The first autumn Greenshanks usually appear at the end of the first week in July and from August to the end of October there is steady movement with a peak in September. The total present in September could be as high as 1,000 birds, but there is a decline

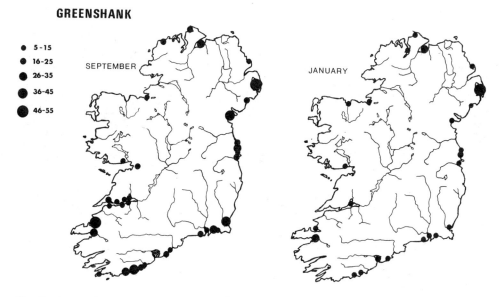

GREENSHANK

- 5-15
- 16-25
- 26-35
- 36-45
- 46-55

SEPTEMBER

JANUARY

Fig. 57. Principal concentrations of Greenshanks in Ireland in September and January. Conventions are as in Fig. 24.

from the end of October and smaller numbers winter. The Irish wintering population is probably in the region of 300-400 birds.

During spring there is some evidence of a very light passage on the north coast (Marsh 1975), but this is not discernible on the east or south coasts at all. The species is very rare in May and June, with the exception of the north coast where a few occur in May.

Greenshanks are quite often found in parties and flocks, particularly in autumn. They prefer to feed in drains instead of on the open mudflats. A few occur inland.

Knot *Calidris canutus*

The Knot is one of those small waders which feed in large flocks, roost in very tight packs and, when flushed, fly up in unison and describe patterns in the sky before settling again. When in large flocks the birds are often difficult to approach, but they are considerably larger than Dunlin, much stockier and with relatively shorter legs. In winter they look greyer than Dunlin. In flight the rump and tail are uniformly greyish, not dark in the centre with white sides like on Dunlin and Sanderling.

The nominate race breeds in Siberia, northern Greenland and Arctic Canada. The Greenland and Canadian birds winter almost entirely in Europe and concentrate in France, the Netherlands, Britain and Ireland where an estimated 579,000 occur (Prater 1974b). Other birds, presumably from Siberia, migrate through the Baltic and along the western European coastline before most move to western Africa to winter. Another race occurs in North America.

In Ireland, unlike the rather similar Dunlin, Knot occur in large numbers at remarkably few estuaries. In autumn they are much more widespread: single birds and small parties occur at brackish lagoons and estuaries from late July to the end of September. Most of these birds are adults, and frequently they show signs of summer plumage. These may well be birds which have gone astray as the main body of Greenland and Canadian birds pass from Iceland to the Waddensea to moult (Prater 1974b).

Very few birds arrive at Strangford Lough and the North Bull, the two main Irish wintering haunts, in August and September. The real increase begins in October and the bulk of the wintering population is present by mid-November (Fig. 58) Although the counts at Strangford Lough show inexplicable fluctuations in some years, counts at the North Bull and Dundalk Bay indicate that there is no obvious passage migration in either spring or autumn. The birds depart quite quickly from the middle of February and virtually none remain by the end of March.

Knot distribution in winter is very limited (Fig. 59). The birds concentrate on the

Three Knot

east coast estuaries and many apparently suitable estuaries on the south coast hold
none at all. Knot are irregular visitors to the Shannon estuary which, like the east coast
estuaries, holds large numbers of Dunlin. The results of ringing in Europe indicate that
our birds originate in Greenland and Canada rather than in Siberia. One ringed in
Wexford in September 1973 was found dead two months later in Mauretania in west
Africa.

There is evidence over the past ten years of a decline and several estuaries which
once held Knot now hold none at all. Dundrum Bay, Co. Down, held up to 700 in
winters 1967-68 and 1968-69 but none since; Cork Harbour had a winter population
of *c*. 3,000 up to 1971-72 but less than 100 in recent years; Courtmacsherry Bay, Co.
Cork, which held up to 200 regularly until 1971-72, now holds none. Numbers at
Strangford Lough fluctuate enormously from year to year but the evidence from the
North Bull and Dundalk Bay suggests a decline in 1974-75, a trend which was also
reflected in Britain and was probably the result of a poor breeding season during 1974
following very cold weather in the Canadian Arctic. The mid-winter total nowadays
might be as low as 25,000 in some years, but in others might be as high as 60,000.

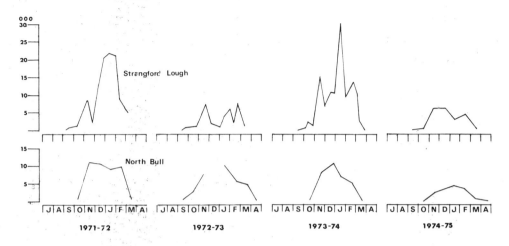

Fig. 58. Numbers of Knot at Strangford Lough and the North Bull, 1971-72 to 1974-75.

Dunlin *Calidris alpina*

The Dunlin is the most abundant shore wader in Ireland and in western Europe. It is the smallest wader likely to be seen in flocks on Irish estuaries; the Sanderling, which resembles it superficially, is slightly larger and prefers open beaches. The Dunlin is rather short-legged but has a fairly long, slightly decurved bill. In winter plumage the bird is generally greyish-brown above with a greyish, streaked breast and white underparts. In summer the back is streaked chestnut and black and there is a black patch on the belly. At all seasons the Dunlin shows a fairly obvious whitish wing-bar and blackish rump and tail with white sides to the rump.

Three races occur in Europe. *C. a schinzii* breeds in Iceland, northern Scandinavia, Britain and Ireland and winters mainly in north-west Africa where the population at that season is estimated at 2-300,000 Dunlin (Pienkowski and Dick 1975). The race *C. alpina* nests in northern Scandinavia and the U.S.S.R. and winters on the Atlantic seaboard of Europe where the total wintering has been estimated at 1,180,000 (Prater 1976b). The wintering area of the third race, *C. a. arctica*, which breeds in eastern Greenland, is still not known.

In Ireland Dunlin are quite thinly distributed breeding birds. There are scattered

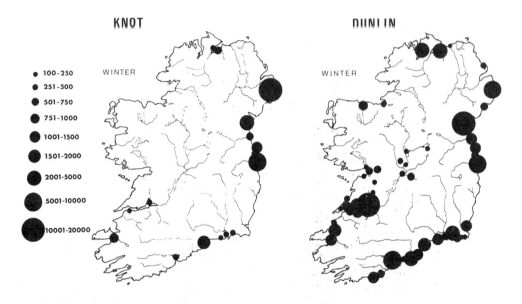

Fig. 59. Principal concentrations of Knot and Dunlin in Ireland in winter.
Conventions are as in Fig. 24.

colonies near lakes and turloughs in the midlands and Connacht and others on the Galway and Mayo coast. Others breed at high altitudes in Donegal and a very few may breed near Lough Neagh.

The first autumn Dunlin, apart from a very few non-breeding birds, arrive back at wetlands in early July and from then until early October there is a steady throughput of birds at most sites. Nowhere are there really large flocks involved, but there is a very obvious turnover. Adults, many of them still showing signs of breeding plumage, predominate until late August. Then, from early October onwards, there is a steady build-up of very large proportions, reaching peak numbers in December, January or February (Fig. 60). After February there is a decrease everywhere and very few Dunlin remain in April. A very obvious passage is noticeable in May, however, at estuaries and marshes all around the coast. Some birds still pass through in the first ten days of June and a few stay the summer at coastal wetlands.

Ringing recoveries and measurements of trapped birds indicate that many of the Dunlin moving through Ireland in the early autumn months of July, August and September are of the race *C. a. schinzii* on their way south to winter in north-west Africa. In winter, birds of the race *C. a. alpina*, breeding in northern Scandinavia and the Soviet Union, are certainly predominant. Whether any Icelandic *C. a. schinzii* or Greenland *C. a. arctica* birds winter is unknown, but the latter race may well be a regular passage migrant. There are three published records, in October, March and May, of these birds in Ireland (Ruttledge 1975) and some British birds, ringed during

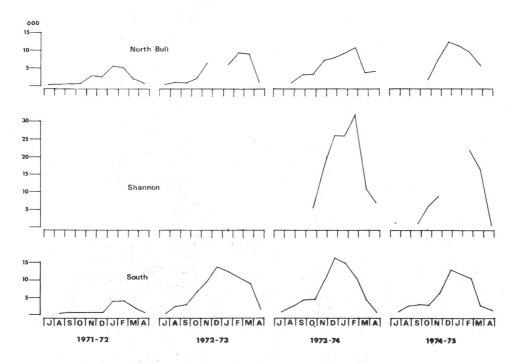

Fig. 30. Numbers of Dunlin at the North Bull, Shannon Estuary and south coast wetlands, 1971-72 to 1974-75.

the same late spring passage in May, have been recovered in Greenland. The position is complicated, however, by the recovery in subsequent winters in Britain of several birds also ringed during the May passage. Only a great deal more ringing will finally solve the problem of the origin of our passage and wintering Dunlin.

The mid-winter population is probably in the region of 100,000-130,000 birds.

Sanderling *Calidris alba*

The Sanderling is superficially very like a Dunlin. It is slightly larger and its shape is rather similar. But it is considerably paler in appearance and its feeding habits are much more active. In winter the upperparts are pale grey with dark markings, particularly at the front of each folded wing where they appear to form 'shoulder-patches'. The underparts are gleaming white. In summer the upperparts are chestnut-brown and the head, neck and upper breast are pale chestnut. In flight the wing-bar is whiter and broader than that of the Dunlin.

Flock of Dunlin landing at roost.

The species is an Arctic breeder, nesting very far north in Europe, Asia and America, and wintering as far south as South Africa, Australia and South America. The western European wintering population has been estimated at 10,000 birds (Prater 1976b).

Although this is quite a widespread species in Ireland, particularly on the west coast beaches, very little is known of its numbers or movements. There is autumn passage in July and August when flocks of 100-200 occur at

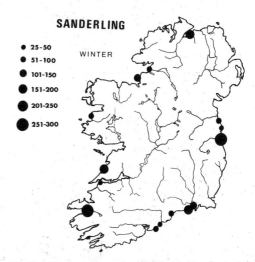

SANDERLING

- ● 25-50
- ● 51-100
- ● 101-150
- ● 151-200
- ● 201-250
- ● 251-300

WINTER

Fig. 61. Principal concentrations of Sanderling in Ireland in winter.
Conventions are as in Fig. 24.

many sites. Numbers are lower in winter, though Fig. 61 severely understates the position in the west, and there is no evidence of any spring passage.

The mid-winter population is probably in excess of 2,000 birds.

Ruff *Philomachus pugnax*

The Ruff is a rather scarce migrant wader in Ireland. In most plumages it is a rather nondescript bird, but the summer-plumaged male, which bears an unmistakeable ruff, is very striking. Birds in this plumage are rarely seen in Ireland, however. In other plumages the Ruff is a brownish, medium-sized wader, very variable in size but about the size of a Redshank and with a shorter bill. In flight there is only a very slight, pale wing-bar, but the white patches on either side of the base of the dark tail are diagnostic. Females and immature birds are smaller than adult males.

The species breeds from Britain, where it is a very rare breeding bird, eastwards into Siberia. In winter it is a great traveller, extending south in large numbers as far as South Africa and Ceylon.

Although England was recolonised in 1963 and over 20 pairs were known to nest in 1971 there has never been any suspicion of breeding in Ireland. Since breeding has been proved in Anglesey and Lancashire on the west coast of Britain colonisation of Ireland in the near future must be very likely.

Ruffs are principally autumn passage migrants to Ireland. They occur, generally in small numbers, at salt marshes, brackish lagoons, turloughs and callows, chiefly in the north, east and south of the country but increasingly in the west as well. Passage usually commences in mid-August and peak numbers occur between mid-September and mid-October. Concentrations of 75-100 have been recorded in this period at Ballycotton, Co. Cork, the Wexford Slobs, Swords, Co. Dublin, and Lough Beg, Co.

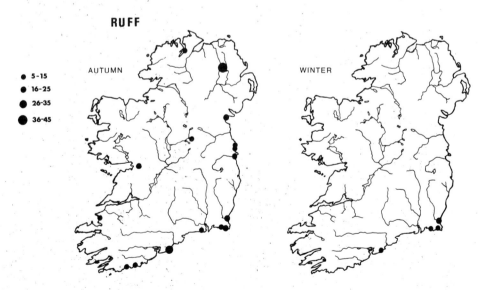

RUFF

AUTUMN

WINTER

● 5-15
● 16-25
● 26-35
● 36-45

Fig. 62. Principal concentrations of Ruffs in Ireland in autumn and winter. Conventions are as in Fig. 24.

Londonderry, but these were in exceptional autumns. In most autumns the peak numbers at any one of these sites does not exceed 40 birds. Numbers taper off rapidly and true wintering is rare. In late November and December even the most favoured sites seldom hold more than one or two birds. There is, however, an arrival in late January and February at several sites, particularly at Ballycotton and in south-east Wexford. In each of these areas up to 40 birds may be present at this time. There is a further spring movement, after these earlier birds have departed, in late March and April. A very few birds may be seen in May, June or July. Males in full breeding plumage are rare but probably now occur every year.

Prater (1973b) has suggested that the arrival in late winter may be of Ruffs which remained in continental Europe after autumn migration until hard weather forced them farther west. These birds have mostly departed by the time the African wintering birds move through in late March and April.

Ruffs have increased considerably in Ireland over the past twenty-five years.

Other Common Waders

Because the intensive wader census work of the past few years has concentrated largely on estuarine species and on the more conspicuous inland species, Lapwing, Golden Plover and Curlew, we have very little new data on birds such as the Snipe *Gallinago gallinago,* Jack Snipe *Lymnocryptes minimus* and Woodcock *Scolopax rusticola* which, although widespread, are skulking and difficult to census, or such as the Purple Sandpiper *Calidris maritima* which occurs exclusively on rocky coasts.

Snipe are common breeding birds throughout the country. Whether native birds winter in Ireland is unknown, but there is a large immigration in autumn and winter of birds from England, Scotland, Iceland and the continent. In hard winters enormous numbers move into Ireland. They frequent bogs, marshes and the fringes of estuaries but their skulking behaviour renders them difficult to observe other than in flight. Jack Snipe are winter visitors and passage migrants as well. They arrive chiefly in October and November and remain into March, sometimes later. Numbers are generally small but single birds occur widely, both inland and on the coast. Woodcock are quite widely distributed breeding birds, but appear scarce or absent in parts of the west and south-west (Sharrock 1976) though counts in Co. Cork in March (Cummins 1974) suggest that the apparent scarcity reflects observer bias rather than a real scarcity. Irish breeding birds are mainly resident but some migrate to Britain and the continent. From late October onwards there is a substantial immigration from Scotland, northern England and Scandinavia and in hard weather much larger numbers are often present. Passage migration has been noted at lighthouses and at Great Saltee Island, Co. Wexford, in late March and April.

Purple Sandpipers are very different from the last three species, being reasonably conspicuous, but their preference for rocky shores which are very difficult to survey thoroughly is the reason for our lack of knowledge of them. They are passage migrants and winter visitors to all coasts of Ireland.

Autumn passage is not very marked, though quite large parties (up to 175) sometimes occur in late March and April. In winter small numbers occur quite widely. The total wintering on the Dublin and Wicklow coast is between 50 and 100 and on the Wexford coast about the same number (O. J. Merne *in litt.*).

A wisp of Snipe

Scarcer Eurasian Waders

As well as those already discussed, a further 17 wader species of European or Asian origin have been recorded in Ireland. Three of these have bred in Ireland, five are annual but scarce passage migrants, mainly in autumn, and the remaining nine are very rare vagrants indeed.

The Dotterel *Eudromias morinellus,* the Avocet *Recurvirostra avosetta* and the Red-necked Phalarope *Phalaropus lobatus* have each bred in Ireland. Dotterels, which are chiefly known as rare autumn passage migrants, bred in 1975. Avocets, although two pairs bred in Wexford in 1938, are now annual vagrants, mainly in winter. A few wintered in Cork Harbour annually from 1956-57 to

1962-63 and in most years to 1969-70, and at the North Bull and Boyne estuary in most years from 1965 66 to 1973 74. Red necked Phalaropes bred in Mayo from 1902 to 1972 and in other counties irregularly. They are rare passage migrants in autumn.

The annual passage migrants are the Green Sandpiper *Tringa ochropus*, Wood Sandpiper *Tringa glareola*, Little Stint *Calidris minutus*, Curlew Sandpiper *Calidris ferruginea* and Grey Phalarope *Phalaropus fulicarius*. All of them occur mainly in autumn, though Green Sandpipers winter regularly in some areas and even spend the summer in a few places. Green and Wood Sandpipers are birds of marshes and small muddy creeks rather than open estuaries where Little Stints and Curlew Sandpipers may sometimes be found in autumn. Grey Phalaropes are hardly birds of wetlands at all: they are seen most often swimming on the surface of the sea in autumn or early winter but as many as 320 have been seen off Cape Clear Island, Co. Cork in a day. Numbers of each of these species fluctuate considerably from one winter to another.

The extreme rarities, together with the number of birds recorded up to 1965 and from 1966 to 1975, are listed in the accompanying Table 34. Comparison with the table setting out the records of rare American waders shows that remarkably few of these rare waders of eastern origin have been seen in recent years despite a great increase in the number of competent ornithologists in the country.

Table 34

Numbers of rare Eurasian waders recorded in Ireland up to 1965 and from 1966 to 1975

	Up to 1965	1966-1975	Total
Sociable Plover *Vanellus gregarius*	2	—	2
Little Ringed Plover *Charadrius dubius*	4	1	5
Kentish Plover *Charadrius alexandrinus*	8	1	9
Great Snipe *Gallinago media*	19	1	20
Temminck's Stint *Calidris temminckii*	11	4	15
Sharp-tailed Sandpiper *Calidris acuminata*	—	1	1
Broad-billed Sandpiper *Limicola falcinellus*	3	—	3
Black-winged Stilt *Himantopus himantopus*	13+	—	13+
Stone Curlew *Burhinus oedicnemus*	16	—	16
	66+	8	74+

Scarcer American Waders

Ireland is one of the most westerly parts of Europe, jutting out into the ocean, face to face across the Atlantic with North America. It is not altogether surprising, therefore, that a number of waders on their autumn migration south from eastern North America should strike the Irish coastline each year when swept across the Atlantic by the storm-track of passing depressions. The enormous increase in the number recorded each year since 1966 is rather surprising, however, especially when compared with the continued scarcity of the rare Eurasian species. A total of 316 American waders was recorded in the 11 years from 1966 to 1976 as compared with the 139 recorded up to 1965. Even allowing for the great increase in observers over the same period this seems an extraordinary increase and it has been argued by Williamson (1975) that changes in the weather pattern over the North Atlantic have been a major factor in increased vagrancy by these birds.

Table 35

Numbers of American waders recorded in Ireland up to 1965 and from 1966 to 1976

	Up to 1965	1966-1976	Total
Killdeer *Charadrius vociferus*	5	3	8
Lesser Golden Plover *Pluvialis dominica*	3	10	13
Dowitcher sp. *Limnodromus sp.*	15	18	33
Long-billed Dowitcher *Limnodromus scolopaceus*	2	1	3
Stilt Sandpiper *Micropalama himantopus*	—	1	1
Upland Sandpiper *Bartramia longicauda*	4	3	7
Eskimo Curlew *Numenius borealis*	1	—	1
Solitary Sandpiper *Tringa solitaria*	—	3	3
Spotted Sandpiper *Tringa macularia*	1	—	1
Greater Yellowlegs *Tringa melanoleuca*	6	2	8
Lesser Yellowlegs *Tringa flavipes*	8	24	32
Least Sandpiper *Calidris minutilla*	2	3	5
Baird's Sandpiper *Calidris bairdii*	1	18	19
White-rumped Sandpiper *Calidris fuscicollis*	15	26	41
Pectoral Sandpiper *Calidris melanotos*	60	121	181
Semipalmated Sandpiper *Calidris pusilla*	—	12	12
Western Sandpiper *Calidris mauri*	2	—	2
Buff-breasted Sandpiper *Tryngites subruficollis*	13	55	68
Wilson's Phalarope *Phalaropus tricolor*	1	16	17
	139	316	455

The number of American waders recorded annually over the 11 years from 1966 has varied enormously. The first year of this period (King 1967) was quite remarkable: the number of Nearctic waders other than Pectoral Sandpipers has only twice been exceeded since despite many more observers now consciously searching for these vagrants. There is scope here for a careful analysis.

Table 36

Numbers of Pectoral Sandpipers and other American waders recorded each year from 1966 to 1976

Year	Pectoral Sandpipers	Others	Total
1966	10	27	37
1967	13	14	27
1968	11	30	41
1969	8	12	20
1970	11	26	37
1971	37	24	61
1972	5	2	7
1973	11	6	17
1974	10	16	26
1975	1	31	32
1976	4	7	11

G. D'A.

OTHER WETLAND BIRDS

As well as the groups usually thought of as wetland birds, the ducks, geese, swans and waders, there are a number of other groups which are dependent to some extent on wetlands. Some, such as divers and gulls, are relatively marine; some, such as herons and Moorhens, frequent even the tiniest wetlands and are extremely difficult to survey; others, such as Great Crested Grebes and Coots, concentrate in winter on larger wetlands and have been somewhat better surveyed. No account, however, can adequately describe the range of species which utilise wetlands and this short chapter only touches on the distribution of the species most obviously dependent on wetlands.

Divers and Grebes

Four species of diver have been recorded in Ireland, but one, the White-billed Diver *Gavia adamsii,* has only been recorded on a single occasion. The Black-throated Diver *Gavia arctica* is an annual but rare winter visitor to bays around the coast. It rarely enters estuaries. The Great Northern Diver *Gavia immer* is one of the two common species and occurs from October to April, with some in September and May and on rare occasions in other months. The Great Northern is most common from the north-east corner of Ireland round the north and west coasts to west Cork. The Red-throated Diver *Gavia*  stellata outnumbers the Great Northern in winter on the east and south coasts and occurs in smaller numbers on the west and north coasts. A few Red-throated Divers breed in Donegal.

Five species of grebe have been recorded. The Great Crested Grebe *Podiceps cristatus* is a common breeding species on shallow lakes, but the range is restricted to the midlands, north and west. Very few breed south of a line from Dundalk to Limerick. The breeding population was censused in 1975 and 756 birds were estimated in the Republic (Preston 1976) and 661 in Northern Ireland (Furphy 1977). Allowing for certain areas which were not adequately covered it is clear that the total population was at least 800 pairs. The winter population is rather differently distributed, with a very large concentration in Cork Harbour, much farther south than the regular breeding area (Fig. 62). Numbers on Lough Neagh are much lower than in summer. Single birds and small parties are quite widely distributed throughout the country in winter.

On the east coast, at Malahide and Carlingford Lough, numbers are much higher in October and November than later, reaching 70-80 birds at each site. This passage may be of birds from Lough Neagh moving south. There is also some evidence of passage in April. Larger numbers have been seen at Dundalk Bay and the Shannon estuary in this month.

The Red-necked Grebe *Podiceps grisegena* is a very rare winter visitor to maritime bays and estuaries. Formerly of annual occurrence, none was recorded from 1972 to 1975 inclusive. The Slavonian Grebe *Podiceps auritus* is a winter visitor in very small numbers to certain marine bays and estuaries, particularly Carlingford Lough, Dublin Bay, Wexford Harbour and Dunmanus Bay, Co. Cork. The Black-necked Grebe *Podiceps nigricollis* is a very rare breeding bird now possibly extinct, and extremely rare winter visitor, not recorded in every year, to coastal bays.

The Little Grebe *Tachybaptus ruficollis* is the commonest grebe. It breeds throughout most of the country, except in high mountainous areas. Outside the breeding season these rather sedentary birds sometimes gather in quite large numbers. The largest regular gatherings recorded during this survey were of 70 on the Wexford Slobs, 60 at Lough Arrow and 40 at Broad Lough, Co. Wicklow, Blanket Nook, Co. Donegal and Lough Owel, Co. Westmeath.

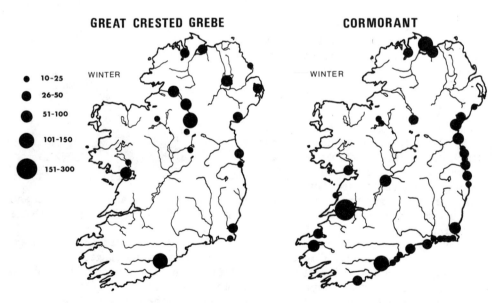

Fig. 63. Principal concentrations of Great Crested Grebes and Cormorants in Ireland in winter. Conventions are as in Fig. 24.

Cormorants and Herons

The Cormorant *Phalacrocorax carbo* is normally considered a seabird and as such is frequently not recorded by waterfowl counters. It breeds around much of the Irish coastline but, apart from a large colony on Lambay Island, it is very scarce on the east coast (Sharrock 1976). The total Irish population in 1969-70 was considered to be 1,865 pairs (Cramp *et al* 1974), though a review of the coverage during the census in those two years indicates that this figure is a serious underestimate. Cormorants tend to disperse in autumn from their colonies, chiefly to the south. Numbers at estuaries are higher in the months of August and September than at any other time, and there is a second smaller peak in February and March which is most noticeable on the south coast.

The Shag *Phalacrocorax aristotelis* is more numerous in Ireland than the Cormorant. Its breeding population was considered to be 2,610 pairs in 1969-70 (Cramp *et al* 1974) and this also was certainly an underestimate. This is a much more marine species than the Cormorant and records from coastal wetlands were restricted to a very few sites: Bannow Bay in Co. Wexford, Tramore Bay and Dungarvan Harbour in Co. Waterford and Galway Bay.

A number of heron species have been recorded in Ireland but the only common species is the Grey Heron *Ardea cinerea,* a widespread breeding bird all over the country. Herons nest mostly in trees, but sometimes on cliffs and in scrub, and feed at streams, rivers, lakes, marshes and estuaries. The numbers recorded on estuaries show

Heron feeding on chicken at Clonakilty town dump

a very marked autumn peak on the east and south coasts. Numbers are highest from July to November, and lowest from February to April when the birds are nesting. This seems to indicate a post-breeding dispersal from small scattered heronries to large wetlands. The largest concentrations of Grey Herons reported were of 100 at Malahide, Co. Dublin and Clonakilty, Co. Cork.

Of the other heron species, the Little Egret *Egretta garzetta* is now an annual vagrant, but the Purple Heron *Ardea purpurea,* Squacco Heron *Ardeola ralloides,* Cattle Egret *Bubulculis ibis,* Night Heron *Nycticorax nycticorax,* Little Bittern *Ixobrychus minutus,* Bittern *Botaurus stellaris* and American Bittern *Botaurus lentiginosus* are all extreme rarities. The Bittern bred in Ireland prior to 1840 and may well be overlooked in its preferred habitat, dense reed-beds. Though not herons, the White Stork *Ciconia ciconia,* Spoonbill *Platalea leucorodia* and Glossy Ibis *Plegadis falcinellus* are quite closely related. The first and last named are very rare, but the Spoonbill is an annual visitor, recorded most often on the south coast and usually in autumn. Birds sometimes remain to winter.

Moorhen, Coot and Rails

The Moorhen *Gallinula chloropus,* much better known as the Waterhen, is an extremely common resident wetland species. It is not gregarious, so does not appear so numerous as the Coot, but it breeds and winters at small ponds and streams as well as on the edges of large rivers and lakes. The breeding population in fact is probably much larger than that of the Coot. No attempt has ever been made to carry out even a sample census because the birds are so widely distributed and spend so much of their time hidden in reed-beds.

The Coot *Fulica atra* is not nearly so widely distributed as a breeding bird because its habitat requirements are more specialised. Coots usually require at least half a hectare of freshwater to breed. They appear to concentrate in very large numbers on certain wetlands in late autumn. Up to 11,500 have been recorded at Lough Corrib in October and 3,800 at Lough Derravaragh in November. There is a decline on these lakes in December and January, though, as is clear from the map (Fig. 64) numbers are still relatively large.

One species of rail, the Water Rail *Rallus aquaticus* is a fairly common resident and winter visitor. It spends most of its time deep in reed-beds where its raucous call is usually the only clue to its presence. The Spotted Crake *Porzana porzana* is a rare vagrant, but may be much overlooked because of its skulking habits, and three other species have been recorded as extreme rarities. The best-known Irish rail, the Corncrake *Crex crex,* is not a bird of wetlands.

Gulls

One of the least studied groups of wetland birds is the gulls. Great Black-backed Gulls *Larus marinus*, Lesser Black-backed Gulls *Larus fuscus*, Herring Gulls *Larus argentatus*, Common Gulls *Larus canus* and Black-headed Gulls *Larus ridibundus* all occur on Irish wetlands. Indeed, they all nest on wetlands too, though Great Black-backed, Lesser Black-backed and Herring Gulls generally prefer marine cliffs. The number of these birds at estuaries, particularly those with large towns or cities nearby, can be extremely high, but little quantitative data are available.

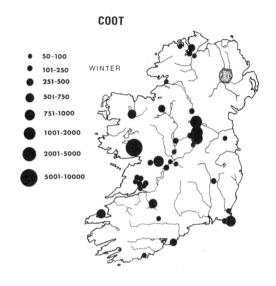

COOT

50-100
101-250
251-500
501-750
751-1000
1001-2000
2001-5000
5001-10000

WINTER

Fig. 64. Principal concentrations of Coots in Ireland in winter. Conventions are as in Fig. 24.

In Dublin Bay Great Black-backed Gulls may number up to 1,000 in winter, Herring Gulls over 10,000, Common Gulls about 2,000 and Black-headed Gulls up to 8,000. Numbers in Cork Harbour are slightly lower, but there have been even fewer counts. In autumn numbers at estuaries are probably higher and much the largest concentrations of Lesser Black-backed Gulls occur. Up to 100 or even many more may be seen on many parts of the south coast, particularly at Lady's Island Lake and Tacumshin where maxima of 1,100 and 600 respectively were recorded during the period of this survey.

Other gull species are scarce on wetlands. The Kittiwake *Rissa tridactyla* is a marine species which usually visits estuaries only for shelter in storms. Little Gulls *Larus minutus* are scarce visitors which are most frequently seen at wetlands on the east and south coasts. Glaucous Gulls *Larus hyperboreus* and Iceland Gulls *Larus glaucoides* are scarce visitors to the coast, usually occurring with flocks of Great Black-backed and Herring Gulls. Glaucous are much more frequent than Iceland Gulls. Several other species of gulls have been recorded in Ireland but all are rare and none can be considered wetland birds.

Terns and Skuas

There are two groups of terns, sea
terns and marsh terns. Five species of
sea tern nest in Ireland — the Common
Tern *Sterna hirundo*, Arctic Tern
Sterna paradisaea, Roseate Tern
Sterna dougalli, Little Tern *Sterna
albifrons* and Sandwich Tern *Sterna
sandvicensis*. Common Terns nest
widely on islands in lakes in the
midlands, west and north but the other
species are almost exclusively coastal
breeders, nesting on marine islands, or
shingle banks. In summer they do not
wander very far from the breeding area,
but there are large post-breeding
congregations of terns in some estuaries

and bays. The largest gathering is probably that in Dublin Bay where up to 10,000
terns roost on Sandymount strand in August and early September. Most are Common
Terns but up to 500 Roseate Terns and some Arctic Terns are also included. These
large flocks also roost at Broad Lough to the south. In summer large numbers of all
five breeding species occur in Wexford Harbour. These are the terns which breed in the
area.

The only regularly occurring marsh tern, the Black Tern *Chlidonias niger*, is a
regular passage migrant on all coasts and inland, but the largest numbers have been
recorded on the east and south coasts. The great majority of birds are recorded in
autumn and spring occurrences are few, though the species has bred in Ireland. The
Black Tern feeds over lagoons and lakes, sometimes in bays and estuaries. The White-
winged Black Tern *Chlidonias leucopterus* is now an annual, but rare, autumn visitor
on the south coast and an even rarer vagrant elsewhere. Four other tern species have
been recorded in Ireland on five occasions or less.

Skuas are not commonly seen at wetlands but all three regular passage migrants
occur at this habitat annually. The Arctic Skua *Stercorarius parasiticus* is most
frequently recorded. On the west and south coasts they regularly harry terns and gulls
at bays and estuaries in autumn; they are quite rare on these habitats on the east and
north coasts. Great Skuas *Stercorarius skua* and Pomarine Skuas *Stercorarius
pomarinus* are less common but regular autumn visitors to wetlands on the same
coasts where they cause mayhem among the gull flocks.

Passerines

Wetlands are an important habitat for many other birds at different seasons. Coastal bays, for example, are usually frequented by Rock Pipits *Anthus spinoletta* and Pied Wagtails *Motacilla alba* which feed on the insects of the upper beach. These birds are also familiar on estuaries, but flocks of finches, Meadow Pipits *Anthus pratensis* and Starlings *Sturnus vulgaris* are usually more noticeable. Hooded Crows *Corvus corone* and Jackdaws *Corvus monedula* scavenge on the tideline. In autumn estuaries are visited by hirundines, Wheatears *Oenanthe oenanthe* and other insect feeders on

migration southwards. The coastal lagoons are more important in autumn for their reed-beds are often used as roosts by large numbers of hirundines and Sedge Warblers *Acrocephalus schoenobaenus* but this aspect of Irish wetlands has not been explored at all.

Inland, Starlings, Meadow Pipits and Hooded Crows are very obvious in winter around most areas of water. In summer Sedge Warblers and Reed Buntings *Emberiza schoeniclus* nest in the reed-beds; the Sedge Warblers emigrate in autumn but the Reed Buntings remain to winter. Hirundines and Swifts *Apus apus* flash back and forth over the water in summer and then also depart. The most typical birds of rivers are perhaps the Kingfisher *Alcedo atthis*, Grey Wagtail *Motacilla cinerea* and Dipper *Cinclus cinclus*. These species may be seen on rivers all year round, though many Kingfishers move to the coast in autumn.

A number of other birds occur at wetlands from time to time and this is far from a complete inventory. Because they are so productive wetlands attract an enormous diversity of species.

CONCLUSIONS

This book has documented in some detail the distribution, numbers and migration of Irish waterfowl and some general conclusions can be drawn from an examination of the individual accounts.

Firstly, it is clear that Ireland is an extremely important wintering area and passage halt for a number of species. Among the ducks, a significant percentage of the north-west European populations of Teal (20%-30%), Wigeon (20%-25%), Shoveler (20%) and Pochard (possibly up to 15%) winter here. Among the geese and swans, some 70% of the Greenland race of the White-fronted Goose, 22% of the European population of the Bewick's Swan and most Icelandic breeding Whooper Swans winter in Ireland. For waders, Ireland is the wintering area for most of the Icelandic breeding Golden Plover and many Icelandic Black-tailed Godwits and Redshanks. Some 15% of the European wintering populations of Bar-tailed Godwits and Redshanks, and perhaps 20% of Europe's wintering Sanderling move into Ireland in autumn. These are all significant percentages of groups of birds which are coming under threat throughout their entire range.

Secondly, Ireland provides a refuge for many birds in cold weather. In the 1962-63 hard winter we know that large numbers of duck, especially Teal, moved to Ireland ahead of the advancing cold weather. Bewick's Swans regularly visit Ireland in greater numbers than usual in cold weather and large immigrations of Lapwing, Golden Plover and Snipe are typical in these conditions. Obviously, Ireland as the most westerly island in Europe south of Iceland is the last refuge for these birds before they turn south, as many did in 1962-63, to attempt in a relatively exhausted condition the hazardous crossing to Spain and Portugal.

Thirdly, Ireland has a number of individual wetlands which are of great importance for their numbers of birds. Those which qualify, under the internationally agreed criteria set out in the Introduction, as of international and national importance are set out in county order in Table 36. Eight of these areas are of outstanding importance. In the Republic six require to be singled out: the Shannon Estuary for its concentrations of ducks and waders, the Little Brosna for its ducks, geese and Black-tailed Godwits, Wexford Harbour and Slobs for their ducks, geese, swans and waders, the North Bull for ducks, geese and waders, Dundalk Bay for waders and Rahasane turlough for wildfowl generally and its uniqueness as the last undrained example of a great wildfowl turlough. In Northern Ireland there are two outstanding sites: Lough Neagh is one of Europe's most important wintering areas for diving ducks and is important for dabbling ducks and swans as well, and Strangford Lough is extremely important for ducks, Brent Geese and waders.

Fourthly, Irish wetlands and their bird populations are subject to a number of threats. Reclamation is undoubtedly the most pressing threat. Arterial drainage schemes are planned for the river systems on which a number of the wildfowl haunts described in this book are located and many haunts have already been drained. Refuse dumping by local authorities is taking place on several estuaries and there are

Brent Geese

proposals for the extension of this activity. *Spartina* continues to spread, engulfing mudflat at most estuaries, and nobody has yet come up with an effective solution. Eutrophication is a growing threat at many midland and western lakes, but its effect on bird populations has not been measureable as yet. Shooting is not a serious problem now that a series of no-shooting areas has been established throughout the country; in any event, most gun-club members are only too aware that a shortage of game birds is detrimental to their interests. Disturbance by boats, especially when these boats carry guns, is, however, a growing problem.

What is to be done? The answer must lie in a clear and detailed policy for wetland conservation throughout the island backed by the governments of both the Republic and Northern Ireland. The key sites for conservation must be identified, and it seems clear that the areas listed in Table 36 all qualify as key sites, and a conservation plan prepared for each. In some cases no action, whether to protect, acquire or manage the area, may be necessary; in others where there are identifiable threats such as arterial drainage or pollution from industrial development, to take two obvious examples, steps must be taken to ensure that the site is protected from the effects of these plans. As well as a policy for wetland conservation there is an obvious need for a strategy for the conservation of certain species which occur widely in small numbers. The most obvious example among the waterfowl of such a species is the White-fronted Goose which has declined sharply at traditional haunts throughout the country apart from the Wexford Slobs. A policy of establishing no-shooting areas at some of the haunts of this goose has been implemented, but a comprehensive management plan is needed. Such a plan will require extensive research.

We have more time in Ireland to conserve our wetlands than the people of most other European countries. Much has been done and continues to be done by the state and by voluntary bodies both north and south of the border but the pace of industrial and agricultural development continues to increase and a wetland conservation policy is an urgent priority if more important sites are not to be lost.

Table 36

Wetlands in the Republic of Ireland and Northern Ireland holding bird populations of international or national importance. This list differs from some published elsewhere due to the re-evaluation of certain sites for which more information has become available.

| | REPUBLIC OF IRELAND | |
County	International Importance	National Importance
CAVAN	Lough Oughter	
CLARE	Ballyallia Lake Shannon Estuary	Mutton Island
CORK	Ballymacoda Cork Harbour	Ballycotton
DONEGAL	Birra Lough Lough Swilly	River Foyle
DUBLIN	Malahide North Bull Rogerstown Estuary	
GALWAY	Lough Corrib Rahasane River Shannon	Portumna
KERRY	Akeragh Lough Castlemaine Harbour Lough Gill Tralee Bay & Barrow Harbour	Lough Leane
LIMERICK	Shannon Estuary	
LONGFORD		Lough Kinale
LOUTH	Dundalk Bay	
MAYO	Lough Carra Inishkea Islands	
OFFALY	Little Brosna River Shannon	

SLIGO	Cummeen Strand Lissadell	
WATERFORD	River Blackwater callows Dungarvan Harbour	River Suir at Coolfin Tramore Waterford Harbour
WESTMEATH	Lough Derrevaragh Lough Owel	Lough Ennel
	Bannow Bay Lady's Island Lake Tacumshin Wexford Harbour and Slobs	
WICKLOW		Poulaphouca Reservoir

NORTHERN IRELAND

International Importance	National Importance
Lough Foyle Lough Neagh Strangford Lough	Lower Lough Erne Upper Lough Erne River Foyle

REFERENCES

Allison, A., Newton, I. and Campbell, C. 1974. *Loch Leven National Nature Reserve*. Chester.

Atkinson-Willes, G. L. 1976. The numerical distribution of ducks, swans and coots as a guide in assessing the importance of wetlands in winter. *Proc. Int. Conf. on Conservation of Wetlands and Waterfowl*. Heiligenhafen, 1974.

Cabot, D. 1967a. The status and distribution of the Greylag Goose *Anser anser* in Ireland. *I. W. C. Publication No. 7*.

——— 1967b. Results of an aerial survey of Irish wildfowl and their wetlands. *I.W.C. Publication No. 8*.

——— 1967c. The status and distribution of the Greenland White-fronted Goose *Anser albifrons flavirostris* in Ireland, January 1967. *I.W.C. Publication No. 9*.

——— **and West, B.** 1973. Population dynamics of Barnacle Geese *Branta leucopsis* in Ireland. *Proc. R. Ir. Acad*. 73, B: 415-443.

Cramp, S., Bourne, W. R. P. and Saunders, D., 1974. *The seabirds of Britain and Ireland*. London.

Cummins, J. 1974. *Woodcock research Ireland*. Nat. Assoc. of Reg. Game Councils. Ireland.

Curran, N. 1968. Survey of wildfowl populations of Lough Erne Basin 1967/68. Duplicated report.

D'Arcy, G. 1978. *Birds at Lough Beg*. Belfast.

Dare, P. J. 1966. The breeding and wintering population of the Oystercatcher (*Haematopus ostralegus Linnaeus*) in the British Isles. *Fishery Invest. Lond*. (Ser. II) 25 (5):1-69.

——— 1970. The movements of Oystercatchers (*Haematopus ostralegus* L.) visiting or breeding in the British Isles. *Fishery Invest. Lond*. (Ser. II) 25 (9):1-137.

Deane, C. D. 1954. Handbook of the birds of Northern Ireland. *Belfast Museum and Art Gallery Bulletin* 1,6: 121-190.

Donker, J. K. 1959. Migration and distribution of the Wigeon *Anas penelope* L. in Europe based on ringing results. *Ardea* 47:1-27.

Eltringham, S. K. and Boyd, H. 1963. The moult migration of the Shelduck to Bridgwater Bay, Somerset. *Brit. Birds* 56:433-444.

Fahy, E., Goodwillie, R., Rochford, J. and Kelly, D. 1975. Eutrophication of a partially enclosed estuarine mudflat. *Marine Poll. Bull*. 6:29-31.

Ferguson, A. 1968. The breeding of the Common Scoter on Lower Lough Erne, Co. Fermanagh. *Ir. Bird Rep*. 1967:8-11.

——— 1971. Notes on the breeding of the Common Scoter *Melanitta nigra* L. in Ireland. *Ir. Nat. J*. 17:29-31.

Flanagan, P. J. and Toner, P. F. 1975. *A preliminary survey of Irish lakes*. Dublin.

Freeman, T. W. 1969. *Ireland, a general and regional geography*. 4th edition. London.

Furphy, J. S. 1977. Census of Great Crested Grebes, Northern Ireland, summer 1975. *Irish Birds* 1:56-58.

Guery, M. D. and Kilty, G. M. 1972. *Zostera* beds at Dungarvan, Co. Waterford. *Ir. Nat. J*. 17:186-193.

Heppleston, P. B. 1971. The feeding ecology of Oystercatchers (*Haematopus ostralegus* L.) in w˙ ʒr i˙ northern Scotland. *J. Anim. Ecol*. 40:651-672.

Hutchinson, C. D. (Ed.) 1975. *The birds of Dublin and Wicklow*. Dublin.

——— **and Keys, J. M.** 1973. The numbers of wildfowl on the North Bull island, Co. Dublin. *Ir. Bird Rep*. 1972:33-43.

——— **and Rochford, J. M.** 1974. The numbers of waders on the North Bull island, Co. Dublin. *Ir. Bird Rep*. 1973:68-71.

Imboden, C. 1974. Zug, Fremdansiedlung und Brutperiode des Kiebitz *Vanellus vanellus* in Europe. *Orn. Beob*. 71:5-134.

Jeffrey, D. (Ed) 1977. *North Bull Island Dublin Bay — a modern coastal natural history*. Dublin.

Jenkins, D., Murray, M. G. and Hall, P. 1975. Structure and regulation of a Shelduck *Tadorna tadorna* population. *J. Anim. Ecol*. 44:201-231.

Kennedy, P. G., Ruttledge, R. F. and Scroope, C. F. 1954. *Birds of Ireland*. Edinburgh.

King, F. 1967. American waders in Ireland, autumn 1966. *Ir. Bird Rep*. 1966:7-11.

Maltby-Prevett, L. S., Boyd, H. and Heyland, J. B. 1975. Observations in Ireland and north-west Europe of Brant from the Queen Elizabeth Islands, N.W.T., Canada. *Bird Banding* 46:155-161.

Marsh, P. J. 1975. Birds of the north coast region. Duplicated report.

Merne, O. J. 1970. The status of the Canada Goose in Ireland. *Ir. Bird Rep.* 1969:12-17.
———— 1971. *Wexford Bird Report, 1970.*
———— 1972. *Wexford Bird Report, 1971.*
———— 1975. *The birds of Wexford.* Wexford.
———— 1977. *The changing status and distribution of the Bewick's Swan in Ireland. Irish Birds* 1:3-15.
Mitchell, G. F. 1976. *The Irish landscape.* London.
Nilsson, L. 1969. The migration of the Goldeneye in north-west Europe. *Wildfowl* 20:112-118.
Norrevang, A. 1959. The migration patterns of some waders in Europe based on the ringing results. *Vidensk Medd. Dansk naturh Foren* 121:181-222.
O'Connor, R. J. and Brown, R. A. 1977. Prey depletion and foraging strategy in the Oystercatcher *Haematopus ostralegus. Oecologia* 27:75-92.
Ogilvie, M. A. 1972. Distribution, numbers and migration. pp. 29-55 in Scott, P. and the Wildfowl Trust. *The Swans.* London.
———— 1975. *Ducks of Britain and Europe.* Berkhamsted.
———— 1978. *Wild Geese.* Berkhamsted.
Perry, K. W. 1975. *The birds of the Inishowen peninsula.* Craigavon.
Pienkowski, M. W. and Dick, W. J. A. 1975. The migration and wintering of Dunlin *Calidris alpina* in north-west Africa. *Ornis. Scand.* 6:151-167.
Prater, A. J. 1973a. *Birds of Estuaries Enquiry 1971-72.* Tring.
———— 1973b. The wintering population of Ruffs in Britain and Ireland. *Bird Study* 22:143-164.
———— 1974a. *Birds of Estuaries Enquiry 1972-73.* Tring.
———— 1974b. The population and migration of the Knot in Europe. *Proceedings of Wader Symposium.* Warsaw. 1973:99-113.
———— 1975. The wintering population of the Black-tailed Godwit. *Bird Study* 22:169-176.
———— 1976a. *Birds of Estuaries Enquiry 1973-74.* Tring.
———— 1976b. The distribution of coastal waders in Europe and north Africa. *Proc. Int. Conf. on Conservation of Wetlands and Waterfowl.* Heiligenhafen. 1974:255-271.
———— 1976c. The breeding population of the Ringed Plover in Britain. *Bird Study* 23:155-161.
———— 1978. *Birds of Estuaries Enquiry 1974-75.* Tring.
Preston, K. 1976. Census of Great Crested Grebes, summer 1975. *Ir. Bird Rep.* 1975:38-43.
Ratcliffe, D. A. 1976. Observations on the breeding of the Golden Plover in Great Britain. *Bird Study* 23:63-116.
Ruttledge, R. F. 1950. A list of the birds of the counties Galway and Mayo showing their status and distribution. *Proc. R. Ir. Acad.* 52, B: 315-381.
———— 1966. *Ireland's Birds.* London.
———— 1970. Winter distribution and numbers of Scaup, Long-tailed Duck and Common Scoter in Ireland. *Bird Study* 17:241-246.
———— 1974. Winter distribution of Whooper and Bewick's Swans in Ireland. *Bird Study* 21:141-145.
———— 1975. *A list of the birds of Ireland.* Dublin.
———— and Hall Watt, R. 1958. The distribution and status of wild geese in Ireland. *Bird Study* 5:22-33.
Salomonson, F. 1968. The moult migration. *Wildfowl* 19:5-24.
Sharrock, J. T. R. (Ed.) 1973. *The natural history of Cape Clear island.* Berkhamsted.
———— 1976. *The atlas of breeding birds in Britain and Ireland.* Tring.
Smiddy, P. 1977. The feeding and roosting of ducks and waders at Ballymacoda, Co. Cork. *Cork Bird Rep.* 1976:38-41.
Stapleton, L. (Ed.) 1975. *Birds of Clare and Limerick.* Limerick.
Szijj, J. 1972. Some suggested criteria for determining the international importance of wetlands in the western Palaearctic. *Proc. Int. Conf. on Conservation of Wetlands and Waterfowl.* Ramsar. 1971:205-216.
Ussher, R. J. and Warren, R. 1900. *The birds of Ireland.* London.
Whilde, T. 1977. *Birds of Galway and Mayo.* Galway.
Williamson, K. 1975. Birds and climatic change. *Bird Study* 22:143-164.
Woolf, W. J. 1966. Migration of Teal ringed in the Netherlands. *Ardea* 54:230-270.
Young, C. M. 1970. Territoriality in the Common Shelduck *Tadorna tadorna. Ibis* 112/330-335.
Young, R. 1975. *Tanymastix stagnalis* (L.) new to Britain and Ireland. *Ir. Nat. J.* 18:203.

INDEX OF PLACE NAMES

All references to Irish place names are indexed

SPECIES INDEX

Only the main accounts of the status of each species are indexed